HOW TO STOP DIETING AND START LIVING

How to Stop Dieting and Start Living

SUE PROSSER

KINGSWAY PUBLICATIONS
EASTBOURNE

Contents

Acknowledgements	7
Foreword	9
Introduction – Building on a Firm Foundation	11
How Best to Use this Book	15
1. Enough is Enough!	17
2. Diets Don't Work	25
3. Weights and Measures	38
4. Eating – a Holistic Experience	47
5. The Feel-good Factor of Food	66
6. Filling the Void	85
7. The Spiritual Void	98
8. Fearful of Being Slim	114
9. Facing the Past	123
10. Mirror, Mirror on the Wall	139
11. An Introduction to Awareness Eating	154
12. Finding Hungry and Finding Full	163
13. Freedom to Choose	193
14. Creating the Right Environment	225
15. A Spirit-controlled Appetite	234
16. Fit For Life FOREVER	242
Appendices	250

Acknowledgements

In order for God to work out His purposes, He has to engineer circumstances so that the right people come together at precisely the right time with the right resources to get the job done.

This is what has undoubtedly happened, both for the founding of Fit For Life Forever and for the writing of this book.

I especially want to thank my team members: Dr David Ford (retired GP); Jessica Castillo-Burley (qualified counsellor); Sharon Fisher (personal fitness trainer) and Sue Raison (delicious home cooking!) for their enormous contributions to the programme. I have bent Dr David's ear on several occasions with my 'What about. . . ?' and 'What ifs?' and every time he has graciously explained medical terms and conditions necessary to my understanding. His firm belief in this programme has given me untold courage.

I want also to thank my pastor (Peter Jacobs) and members of my local church for being my 'guinea pigs' and supporting me in this venture from the start.

Thanks to Gilly, not only for being my 'thin friend' but for agreeing to be interviewed for this book.

Thanks also to Solana for her professional critique of the book and Sally, a Fit For Life Forever study group leader, for her constructive encouragement.

Thank you, too, to other Christian writers who have inspired me through their own insights, especially confirming my own deep-seated hunch that dieting was counter-productive and that what God was showing me was both biblical and effective.

Last, but certainly not least, I wish to thank my husband, David. Living with someone so conscientious about eating as I am must have been a trial at times! Talk about 'This is your conscience speaking. . . !' He has not only survived this, but has lost a considerable amount of weight himself. Well done! We have worked together in Christian ministry for 30 years, always in honour and love preferring one another. His support for me, practically, emotionally and spiritually, has been immeasurable.

Foreword

Here is a new and exciting approach to all kinds of disordered eating. It is based on the principle that diets do not work in the long run, most of them ending in failure and disappointment. This book and the corresponding course deal with how unhelpful eating habits develop, hunger management, appetite signals and nutrition. It is not limited to weight reduction but is helpful for any eating problem.

Health problems caused by obesity and inappropriate eating are explained and also how the body can benefit from sensible eating in terms of lowered blood pressure, improved mobility and increased life expectancy.

The course is based on biblical principles with the emphasis on freedom rather than a set of rules. As a result, people have found a new freedom to enjoy their food without pressure from any source, past or present. Course participants have generally been increasingly able to regulate their own weight and have seen encouraging results.

As a medical doctor, and also as a Christian, I have no hesitation in recommending this course to all who are interested in having a Spirit-controlled appetite and a healthy lifestyle.

Dr David Ford, GP

Introduction – Building on a Firm Foundation

Weight regulation is complex and involves a whole range of issues: physical, hormonal, environmental, genetic, emotional, social and spiritual. The challenges of writing a Christian book on this subject have been to address such complexity without being complicated, to be simple without being simplistic, to be analytical about the problems and the failure of the diet industry to offer workable solutions, and then to point the reader to God as the One who can help us find our way through the fog and succeed where everything else has failed.

This spiritual thread, woven throughout the fabric of the book, holds the whole entity together. Pull it out, and everything else will just fall apart! God is profoundly interested in every aspect of our lives and waits only to be invited in, in order for us to know His enabling power. Allow me, therefore, to introduce you to four spiritual truths which are foundational to the teaching given in this book. These are:

1. We are each God's unique creation.
2. He loves us unconditionally.
3. He wants us to live in freedom, to be healthy, to look our best, and to succeed in our weight-management goals.
4. God's Word (the Bible) can help us overcome our disordered eating and maintain a healthy lifestyle.

Even when these spiritual truths are taken into consideration, it is still easy to over-simplify issues. There are those who would have us believe that all overeating is due to sinful indulgence, while others take the line that overeaters are simply sublimating their deep-seated hunger for God with food. Both of these suppositions are true to a point, yet they provide only part of the picture. There are medical and genetic issues to be considered – the satiety factor of various foods, deeply ingrained thought patterns, and a whole range of human emotions. Certainly we shall consider the spiritual, but we shall look at many other issues as well, always bearing in mind that God's solutions are often extremely practical. It is this balance that I wish, through my writing, to convey.

The principles taught in these pages have first been applied to my own life. Not only have I permanently lost 60 pounds in weight, so that I am now a normal weight and slimmer than I have ever been, but food has also lost its magnetism and found its rightful place in my life.

Out of my own experience of achieving this weight loss without dieting, and what I believe to be a direct commission from the Lord, Fit For Life Forever was launched in late 2004. A growing number of individuals and groups, both in the UK and other parts of the world, are now discovering these invaluable keys to understanding their weight control issues. Testimonies affirm that not only are they being freed from their bondage to food, diets and overeating, but are finding healing and freedom in many other areas and experiencing new depths in their relationship with the Lord.

As you study this programme, several things in relation to food and eating are going to happen:

1. You will discover why you have developed disordered eating habits.
2. You will be set free from a 'diet mentality' which brings guilt and shame.
3. You will learn how to say no to food you don't need.
4. You will begin to recognise and correct the faulty and unhelpful thought patterns which have governed your eating habits.
5. You will learn to recognise 'inner hunger' and to satisfy it more appropriately.
6. You will learn how to observe and correct your own eating patterns so that you eat primarily for physiological reasons.

It is my prayer that reading this book will inspire you with hope and confidence so that you, too, can achieve your weight goals and enjoy a fit and healthy life.

How Best to Use this Book

You will probably want to read through this material in the normal way to gain an overview of what this book is all about. But then I advise you to go through it again, slowly, being conscientious to answer the questions at the end of each chapter. If the Lord is revealing things to you, stay with it until you feel it is time to move on. (See below for supplementary material.)

You will observe that I do not actually teach any technique for non-diet weight loss until Chapter 10. If you wish to get underway with the practical before studying and applying the analytical, soul-searching teaching of Chapters 4–9, this is understandable and perfectly in order. You should realise, however, that your success in applying these principles will probably be much greater once you have allowed God to deal with your inner hindrances to weight regulation, as instructed in the earlier part of the book.

The Fit For Life Forever Course

This course is suitable for individuals, home study groups and church outreach programmes. Using this book as the primary textbook, the course condenses the teaching into twelve units. There is a range of support materials which include:

- A twelve-unit workbook and a twelve-week Daily Devotional Guide. The Home Assignments from *How to Stop Dieting* are also included in the workbook, which can be downloaded as an e-book from the website (see below).
- A nutritional and physical exercise supplement to help you to make informed choices and give you a healthier lifestyle.
- A Powerpoint slide presentation pack available as a teaching aid for group leaders.
- A DVD of the Fit For Life Forever seminar.

To find out more visit the Fit For Life Forever website: www.fitforlifeforever.org or www.f4lf.org and download our free 'How to Run a Fit For Life Forever Course' document. Or write to me at Fit For Life Forever, c/o Christian Gospel Church, PO Box 143, Gosport PO13 9UN.

You may also wish to organise a one-day or weekend seminar where the principles of this book are taught personally by the author. This is often an excellent way of initiating a local group.

Note: 'Fit for Life Forever' as used throughout this book refers to the generic name of my ministry, of which *How to Stop Dieting and Start Living* is a primary resource.

1

Enough is Enough!

'Good heavens!' I declared, gazing down at the bathroom scales in horror. 'It can't be as bad as that!'

I knew that in the last two months I must have put on a lot of weight, because I had recently been out to buy a new skirt and discovered, for the first time in my life, that I needed a size 20. But without having any scales to weigh myself, I hadn't known just how bad the damage was. Now, this moment of self-discovery sent a wave of panic over me.

'Fourteen stone, one pound! No, that can't be right,' I muttered to myself, gazing down at the digital bathroom scales we had just purchased the day before. I had resisted weighing myself immediately we had got them home, reasoning (as seasoned dieters will understand) that since it was towards the end of the day I was bound to weigh more than I would first thing in the morning. No, I would wait – far better to weigh myself, without clothes, when I would be at my lightest!

Although the weigh-in revealed a new all-time high in my struggle against excess weight, in truth it wasn't vastly different to my previous all-time high a few years before. That was in 1998, when, having reached thirteen stone, ten pounds, I had taken myself off to my doctor and asked him to put me on a diet. He had weighed me, made a sucking motion with his pursed lips, shaken his head and told me that I was 'clinically obese'. How I hated that word – far kinder just to call it 'being overweight' but I was in denial to an extent. Then he packed me off to the weight clinic where I would be under the watchful eye of a nurse. My blood pressure, I discovered, was also too high, but he held off giving me medication in the hopes that losing weight would do the trick.

The nurse gave me a diet sheet telling me which foods to avoid and an upper limit guide as to the recommended intake of various individual items. It was all very simple, and all I had to do was to keep a food diary and report back every week for a weigh-in and a pep talk. It cost nothing, was only mildly inconvenient and, best of all, it was private.

Under the watchful eye of the practice nurse I did indeed lose weight – about one kilogramme (or just over two pounds) a week, overall. She was kind and sympathetic, but even when I had done well with my weight loss she would look through my food diary and pull me up for having that odd pastry crust or dish of ice-cream. The satisfaction of having lost weight was taken away by these mild repri-mands. After four weeks she reduced my visits to once a fortnight, and then after about eight visits, when I had lost weight consistently every time, she cut me loose. 'You seem to be managing very well,' she said, encouragingly. 'I don't think you need me any more. Keep it up!' And with that I was back on my own.

I did, indeed, try to 'keep it up'. I was under twelve stone, and had vowed *never* to be thirteen stone ever again. But I had said that once before, back in 1986, when I had weighed thirteen stone, five pounds. Clearly I hadn't kept my vow on that occasion, and this time, sadly, was to prove no different.

I didn't put the weight back immediately; in fact for a while I did continue to lose weight under my own steam and got down to around eleven stone, seven pounds. But slowly, imperceptibly, it had taken a turn upwards, until – before I knew it – I was back at around twelve and a half stone. And there, in spite of all my efforts to diet, I remained stuck! By now I had turned 50 and was menopausal. For me dieting was like trying to ladle water out of a sinking boat. The minute difference I was able to make by slavishly following one diet regime or another was counteracted, so it seemed, by the inevitability of age-related weight gain. I finally resigned myself to staying fat.

But being fat was one thing, putting on a further 20 pounds was another! And so now, on that cold January morning in 2004, as I dejectedly stepped off my brand new set of digital scales and gazed at my sorry form in the full-length mirror, I cried out to God for help. I might be in my mid-fifties, but surely I didn't have to settle for this. I looked, and indeed felt, awful.

The last time I had weighed myself previous to this had been only two months earlier, when my husband David and I had been living in Tanzania. Then I was twelve stone, seven pounds and I had been consciously trying to lose a few pounds if I could. So what had gone wrong? Why had I managed to put on 22 pounds in less than eight weeks?

And given this rapid rate of weight gain, what might happen in the next eight weeks? If I knew the answer to the 'why?' then I might be better equipped to avoid the same pitfalls in the future. Along with my prayer for God to help me to lose weight, I prayed that He would show me the causes for my weight gain. The revelation that He gave was to completely change my life.

* * *

We had been so happy as we stepped on board the plane bound for Dar-es-Salaam, Tanzania. This was the 3rd June 2004, and we were going out to work as missionaries for an indigenous African church which was seeing phenomenal growth and amazing miracles. How privileged we felt to be a part of this revival! Three times previously we had visited the work short-term, before committing ourselves to actually taking up residence and coming under the authority of this group. Our brief was to help strengthen existing churches and to plant new ones and we were looking forward to at least five years of fruitful ministry.

We were not green to this sort of work. We had served as missionaries, in one capacity or another, for the past 26 years, including a six-and-a-half-year spell in Zimbabwe, so we felt that we knew pretty well what we were letting ourselves in for. However, things went badly wrong for us and we finally accepted the advice of our leadership back in the UK to come home. We had been on the mission field for a mere six months, had nothing to show for it and we both felt failures.

Coming home unexpectedly as we did, we were unable

to return immediately to our own home, which we had rented out, and so we accepted the offer of a vacant flat belonging to a Christian friend. What a godsend this was! Here we were able to relax and recover from our wounds and also to seek God for the future direction of our ministry.

But what future? It would be comparatively easy for Dave, I thought, because he could just continue his short-term missions to various countries as he always had done. But for me it didn't seem that simple. For one thing, being a woman, I didn't have the same opportunities for ministry as David. In the past I had developed a ministry in song and had received several original songs from the Lord, which had been a blessing to many; but now my voice was losing its quality and I didn't feel as comfortable singing solo. Up until the point when we had gone to Tanzania I had also worked as a supply teacher when we were at home, but with the downward spiral in school discipline over the years and the resulting contempt that many children seemed now to have for temporary staff especially, I had been glad to resign totally from the teaching profession. There was no way that I wanted to go back into a classroom again.

So, why am I telling you all of this? Because, in retrospect, it was a major factor in my weight gain. The feelings of failure and disappointment at having to return from Tanzania, the lack of vision for the future, the sense of being 'washed up'. . . all of this added up to one particular form of over-indulgence – COMFORT EATING!

But that wasn't all; there were many others factors all coming into play. For one thing I was *bored*. Obviously, coming home at short notice we had been unable to plan any work for when we returned. There were a number of churches in the UK where we ministered from time to time, but on the run-up to Christmas they would have their own programmes. It wasn't a good time for visiting speakers. And so we basically just hung around. No one condemned us for this, and in truth we did need a bit of space to collect ourselves again, but we were living in someone else's home so there wasn't much I could do to keep myself occupied.

Christmas was on the horizon, and this gives another clue as to the contributory factors in my weight gain. The supermarkets were full of *festive delicacies*, all of them bursting with calories! I might have waited until the season was well and truly upon us, but out in Tanzania we had had to forego several foods and live on quite a basic diet. Being suddenly exposed to such a huge variety of food and having our memories jogged over things which we used to eat and enjoy, we simply cast off all restraint and overdosed on the lot! This is called *scarcity eating*, which often follows a time of deprivation.

As we entered into the New Year we did have some work lined up, but before embarking on this we decided to have a short, cheap holiday on a Mediterranean island. The weather was dismal, the landscape barren and the hotel mediocre. But there was one plus factor in the scenario – eat-as-much-as-you-like, buffet-style meals! The food wasn't good – just cheap and plentiful and laden with salt, sugar and fat to make it palatable. So I simply stuffed my face! Why? Because I simply had to *get my money's worth*! I had also decided that since my commitment to losing weight would begin the day after I got home, this holiday should serve as a prolonged 'Last Supper' making the most of my opportunity to binge because restrictions lay up ahead!

Although your situation may be vastly different from the one which I have described, do you perhaps identify with some of my reasons for overeating? Comfort, boredom, nationally-sanctioned binges, rebound from deprivation, wanting to get your money's worth and the 'Last Supper' . . . and there are many more reasons why many of us eat unnecessarily, which we will talk about later.

Trying to look back over a lifetime of weight gain and dieting, it would have been far more difficult to identify the factors which had contributed to my problems, but experiencing such a sudden and dramatic increase in weight over a short period of time gave me a window, restricted yet clear enough to identify what was going on. It also led me into *awareness eating* – a way of observing my eating behaviour in order to see what was working *for* me and what was working *against* me. This has formed the basis of the Fit For Life Forever principles of weight regulation expounded here in this book. But best of all, it has freed me from diets for good!

Home Assignments

1. Your story – then and now. We each have a story to tell. My own journey to freedom began by looking back to see where things had gone wrong. Your journey may take you back to childhood, or it may focus on more recent events. Write it down or share your thoughts with a sympathetic listener.

2. I want you to look analytically at your present eating habits. So, to this end, it would be beneficial for you

to complete the Meal Observation Log in Appendix 1, applying it to as many meals as possible over the coming days. It will only take about ten minutes to complete and will probably be a real eye-opener for you. The more thorough you are, the more accurate will be the picture of your eating habits which will emerge. Please don't make it burdensome for yourself, but I am sure that you will find that the more committed you are to completing this and subsequent exercises, the better will be your overall results.

2

Diets Don't Work

If you want to lose weight, you have to go on a diet, right? WRONG!

Let me wait a moment and let that sink in! I can almost hear your brain ticking over. . . 'But there isn't any other way, is there?' you're probably reasoning. 'It's just a case of finding the *right* diet and then sticking to it.'

Well, is that what you were thinking? The fact is that, up until now, you've probably tried all sorts of diets to help you regulate your weight, but you've either thrown in the towel or gained back all the weight you managed to lose (plus a few more pounds besides), and this has led you to the conclusion that either that particular diet didn't work or you weren't sufficiently disciplined to stick to it. And when over a period of time you've simply regained all the weight you managed to shed, you've probably concluded that you simply lacked the willpower and branded yourself a failure. What you perhaps never realised was that by repeating this pattern of behaviour and thought you were compounding your problem time and time again, making it ever more difficult for you to succeed. But it isn't you that is the failure. Diets, by their very nature, set us up to fail.

I don't know how many diets there are or have been on the British market, but in the USA there are apparently over 30,000 to choose from![1] What does this tell us?

First of all, it lets us know that there is an enormous market out there for slimming aids. It is estimated that over half of the adult population in the UK may be on a diet at any one time, and with 75% of the adult population (according to government figures) currently being overweight (20% obese) this is highly probable.[2] Add to this those who diet to achieve a certain body image when they don't need to (especially teenage girls) and we see a very lucrative market indeed. Allowing for the fact that there are some diets which are plain whacky, or dangerous, or both, one would expect, if dieting actually worked, for there to be evidence of some statistical improvement in the national state of things, but there isn't. Instead, in spite of a massive drive to make us more health conscious, the problem seems to be getting steadily worse.

But do diets work for some people? Undoubtedly, yes, for a minority they do, and such people are to be applauded for their sheer tenacity and willpower. But most people are not so lucky. It is estimated that only about ten dieters in a hundred actually reach their weight goal, and eight of these will eventually, over the next five years, regain all that they have lost, several of them much more quickly than that. Which of us would invest money in some enterprise which

---

[1] Anderson, Sally, 'Why Most Diets Don't Work', on Personal MD.com website: www.personalmd.com (accessed 28/11/06)

[2] House of Commons Health Committee (2004)

offered us only a 2% possibility of success? Yet we go from diet to diet, investing our time and money hoping for permanent results, only to be disappointed time and time again. (Of course, if you were investing your money in weight loss products you might do very well indeed!)

The failure of diet regimes to bring about any lasting results is borne out in a report by the British Dietetic Association in 2004.[3] It surveyed 4,000 men and women and found that:

- Over one quarter were constantly fighting the bulge.
- Nearly 40% of women had put back on more weight than they had lost.
- Nearly 20% of men had put back on more weight than they had lost.
- 10% put back on more than a stone on top of their pre-diet weight.
- Only 20% actually stuck to a diet for more than a month.
- 10% stuck to a diet for eight weeks or more.

Well, do you identify with any of that? If you do, then you are simply adding weight (pardon the pun) to the argument that diets don't work!

An American author, Dr Bob Schwartz, in his book entitled *Diets Don't Work*[4] tells how he ran a health spa for 20 years and, as part of his regime, would put people on various diets. He discovered, in common with what many have

---

[3] 'Fat Plan Diet' (11/07/04), on the website: www.pharma-lexicon. com/medicalnews.php?newsid=10565 (accessed 28/11/06)

[4] Schwartz, Bob, *Diets Don't Work* (Breakthru Publishers, first edition 1982)

maintained, that even though people often successfully shed weight on his prescribed diets, most clients put the weight straight back on – a constant source of frustration and puzzlement. So Dr Schwartz decided to test his diets on himself, even though he did not personally have a weight problem. In one week alone he lost eleven pounds. Then he stopped dieting and gradually, over about two months, he regained the weight. He tried out another one of his diets, and this time he had similar though less dramatic results. But then he noticed something – his clothing was becoming tight on him, and for the first time in his life he now needed to go on a diet! He wasn't too concerned initially, reasoning that all he needed to do was to return to the first diet through which he had previously lost eleven pounds. But this time the same diet only lost him one pound! What's more, when he stopped the diet he immediately regained several pounds! He had discovered for himself what many of us have found by experience, that each time we have gone on a diet we have lost weight more slowly and gained it back faster – often with interest! Ironically, Dr Schwartz did find that diets worked for some people – those who had come to him wanting to find some way of gaining weight!

But why does this phenomenon happen? Dr Schwartz was writing in the 1970s, when comparatively little was known about the science of weight regulation, but now, although we are dealing with a very complex issue, we understand that it has a lot to do with how our bodies metabolise. Metabolism can be defined as the way in which your body processes food. The amount of energy that you need is determined by your 'Basal Metabolic Rate' (BMR) which is the amount of energy your body needs just to function and renew itself. Our overall metabolic rate will be higher than this since it must take into account the fuel needed for the day's activities, which varies according to an individual's lifestyle. When a person goes on a diet this almost always involves a drastic cut in the number of calories consumed. This is especially true of 'wonder diets' – those which promise phenomenal weight loss in a very short period of time. This cut is achieved either by counting the number of calories taken in and limiting them to a certain measure, or by cutting out certain foods which are known to be high in calories. The result is that the body does initially lose weight. However, as the body becomes aware of this reduction in calorific intake it compensates by slowing down the metabolism and putting it into what is known as 'starvation mode'. This is a self-protection mode which causes the body to burn fuel at a slower rate and to store what fuel it does receive as fat.

What is more, the body, having used up over the first few days its surplus store of carbohydrates stored as glycogen, does not turn exclusively to the body's fat store for fuel, but begins also to take its energy from the muscles, depleting them of protein and other nutrients. When the protein is broken down it releases nitrogen which is washed away by water taken from tissue cells. This water loss does indeed affect the scales and create the impression of weight loss. However, the water is quickly restored through drinking, while the depletion of muscle tissue creates further problems for our metabolism. Why is this?

Our muscles burn up to five times as many calories as fat does (50 calories per pound per day as opposed to ten or eleven calories per pound for fat). Therefore, to lose muscle mass makes the whole metabolic process less efficient. The effect is that the same reduced intake of calories begins to produce fewer results! This is why some slimming clubs, in order to help you to achieve your weight goal (even if it is unrealistic) will, when you have started to plateau, often reduce your calorie intake even more. They know that the lower you can take your weight the less likely you are to maintain it without their help, so your dependency is secured. But in the long term constantly reducing your intake of calories only exacerbates the problem, making it harder and harder for your body to burn fat tissue.

But there is even worse news. Once the diet is over and normal eating is resumed, if weight is regained it is not regained as muscle but as fat. The muscle can only be regained by exercise, but this in itself becomes more arduous the greater the weight gain and so we have a vicious circle known as 'Weight Cycling', as seen in Figure 1.

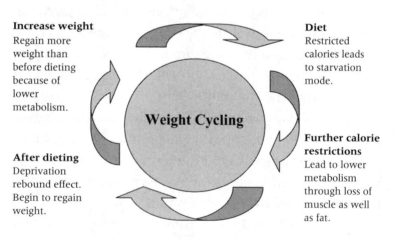

Increase weight
Regain more weight than before dieting because of lower metabolism.

After dieting
Deprivation rebound effect. Begin to regain weight.

Weight Cycling

Diet
Restricted calories leads to starvation mode.

Further calorie restrictions
Lead to lower metabolism through loss of muscle as well as fat.

Figure 1 – Weight Cycling

Let us suppose, by way of example, that you went on a strict calorie-reduction, deprivation-style diet and managed to lose 15 pounds. If this weight loss was from the muscle tissue, rather than your fat cells, then after the diet your body would need 600 calories less than it did previously, just to maintain the weight loss. However, if you lost the weight more slowly through a combination of sensible eating and exercise designed to maintain and build muscle tissue, then you probably wouldn't need fewer calories at all when you reached your target weight. The lost fat tissue would only reduce your calorie needs by 150 per day, but over against this a muscle gain of just four pounds would adequately compensate for the loss. If we don't understand this process and don't exercise, but return to eating what we might consider a 'sensible amount', similar to what we ate before needing to diet, then unfortunately we may well put weight back on, often in excess of what we initially lost.

Another thing that we need to understand about metabolism is that the body naturally slows up with age. A man who might consume 3,400 calories aged 25, may only need around 2,000 calories when he is 70. This is a drop of 40%. Not only does our Basal Metabolic Rate become less, but we are using up fewer calories doing exercise and work. We simply cannot, therefore, eat the same amount of food as we did in our youth and early adulthood without suffering the consequences. Many experts believe that, due to changes in our lifestyle and metabolism, we have a tendency from about the age of 26 to gain an extra half pound of fat a year and lose the equivalent in muscle. If that is true, it means that by the time we reach 40, we have seven extra pounds of fat on the body, even if we actually weigh the same. However, since a pound of fat is of a much larger mass than a pound of muscle, even though you might weigh the same as 14 years ago the same clothes will not fit you. You will probably be a size bigger!

The Psychological Effect of Dieting

'Okay,' you say, 'now that I understand how it works, I'll simply adjust my food intake accordingly, or I'll make sure that I exercise as well as diet, so that I'll build up and maintain my muscles.' This is good, sound reasoning, and all very well, if you can pull it off. But there is one thing which is powerfully working against you, and that is the compulsion which diets, by their very nature, incite in the passions of their adherents, to swing to the opposite extreme as soon as the restraints are taken away.

Think about it. Diets involve a strict adherence to a set of rules: 'You mustn't eat this, you can't touch that'; 'Only have a thousand calories a day'; 'Don't mix your proteins with your carbohydrates'; 'Stick to X amount of points'. They also label foods under the general heading of 'good' or 'bad' and make us feel as though we have committed a sin if we eat the forbidden items. There is one diet which, indeed, labels high-calorie / low-nutrient foods as 'sins' but allows you to have a certain number of sins per day! While given permission by the diet to eat such foods, there is the implication that to do so is still slightly naughty, setting you up for a guilt trip when the sin allowance is exceeded! It probably affects Christians worst of all, because we take sin seriously.

We can live with these kinds of restraints for a period of

time, but eventually we start to rebel when we see that our
primary physical and emotional needs are not being adequately met. But such 'rebellion' is not sin; it is a natural
response to having our boundaries invaded and our auton-
omy taken away:

> When a diet doctor or a diet plan invades your boundaries, it's
> normal to feel powerless. The longer you follow the food
> restrictions, the greater the assault on your autonomy. . . and
> you will likely rebel by eating more.[5]

So, when we have been curbing our desire to eat the kinds
of food we most enjoy and limiting our intake so much as
to remain hungry and unsatisfied, our inner drive to have
these needs met is heightened and we desire what we can't
have more and more.

After we have been deprived of the foods we want most
for some time, a number of things starts to happen. First, we
become preoccupied with food, to the point that our whole
life revolves around the diet and we have difficulty concentrating on anything else. We become hypersensitive to the
sight and smell of food. Then we desire it more and more,
craving especially those foods which are intensely flavoured,
high in sugar and fat, and easily digestible. This, in turn, can
lead to compulsive eating, which is an over-compensation
for our previous deprivation, and if this pattern continues
unaddressed it may be the start of such medically recognised eating disorders as binge eating, bulimia and
anorexia.

---

[5] Tribole, Evelyn and Resch, Elyse, *Intuitive Eating* (St Martin's
Griffin, 1995)

Once we have given in to those food cravings, we suffer psychologically because failure fills us with guilt and shame. This stress only adds to our trauma, making us eat even more to satisfy our emotional need for comfort. It is another vicious circle from which there seems to be no escape.

In order to help you grasp hold of this idea of deprivation and compensation, consider for a moment another powerful drive which we humans experience – the need for sleep. What happens if one night you don't get enough sleep? The next day you might not function so well, and you would be hoping to make it up the following night. But suppose that the next night you also have a disturbed sleep, followed by the next and then the next. Now you're really in trouble! All you can think about is how tired you feel and how you long to get more sleep. You might become irritable and you would find it very hard to concentrate. Your desire for sleep has now become a craving. Eventually you do get a good night's sleep, with no disturbances. But now the usual seven or eight hours are not enough – you want to sleep for hours and hours to make up for what was lost, and you will probably want to do this for several nights before getting back on track. In fact, you could say, you would have a 'sleeping binge'!

Do you see the comparison between your need for sleep and your need to be satisfied with the kinds of food you enjoy? Always, following a period of deprivation, there will be a natural inclination to overcompensate. But when we overcompensate regarding our food, it wreaks havoc with our metabolism and our problem just gets worse and worse.

Dieting is a Losing Battle!

There are at least three more reasons why diets don't generally work. If you think back to my original testimony you will recall how my weight gain was primarily to do with the fact that I had been feeding my head and my heart, not just my physiological need. Had I decided to go on a prescribed diet I would doubtless have lost weight for a time, but once off the regime those old thought patterns – such as having to eat in order to get my money's worth – would have sprung into action again and I would have been defeated without knowing why. You see, *diets only address symptoms; they do not deal with the root causes.* They seek to bring about cosmetic changes, but are powerless in changing mental attitudes or dealing with emotional needs which may have caused the weight increase in the first place. I shall have far more to explain concerning these matters at a later place, but for now suffice to say that, unless the roots are addressed and dealt with, you are almost certainly going to revert to your old ways once you come off a diet. I want to make you aware of why you are eating when you don't really need to and why you consume more than your body requires. Not only will you be shown why these things have affected your weight, but you will be given powerful tools to enable you to deal with those roots so that they no longer negatively affect your eating.

Another cause of failure when we seek to follow a prescribed programme of weight regulation is that *there is no such thing as a one-size-fits-all diet.* I get very frustrated at times by claims which speak of the 'average' man or woman, without there being any attempt to qualify what 'average' means. Does it mean, that which applies to most people (the mode), or the actual need of the middle person when scores are ranked (the median), or is it where all the individual scores are added up and divided by the number that took part (the mean)? Statistics can mean virtually anything without due qualification!

I have read, for instance, that the daily amount of calories needed for the 'average' woman is around 2,000, but this takes no account of her age, size or lifestyle. I may have needed that amount once, when I was younger, but now, as well as requiring fewer calories due to natural ageing, I could need in the region of 600 calories per day less than previously simply because I have lost 60 pounds in weight and therefore have less body mass to maintain. Furthermore, some days I am very active and other days I sit at my computer most of the time. If I were religiously consuming a certain number of externally imposed calories, believing that was what my body always needed, I could be way out in my calculation.

Finally, there is a most important root cause, which we should not overlook. It is this: that each of us has 'inner hungers' which can neither be satisfied through food, nor through company, excitement, material possessions, fame or fortune. Again, we will be dealing fully with this at a later point but, for now, just know that the God who created you did so in order that you might enjoy friendship with Him in a personal, deeply satisfying way. If this discovery has evaded you so far, either through ignorance or cynicism, it need not always be the case. Through the Fit For Life Forever principles you will have the opportunity to prove for yourself the reality of God's power and love as He helps you achieve what every diet you have ever tried has failed to do. As you 'taste and see that the Lord is good' (Psalm 34:8), you will be encouraged to trust Him more and more, and you will find that hitherto elusive answer to your quest for inner satisfaction.

Home Assignments

1. Make a list of some of the diet regimes you have followed. For each one, answer these questions: (a) How long did you stick to the diet for? (b) Did you lose any weight? (c) Did you put the weight back on and, if so, in what amount of time? (d) Did you eventually put back on more weight than you lost?
2. Which of the following effects of dieting have you experienced? (a) A sense of deprivation (b) Preoccupation with food (c) Food cravings (d) Binge eating.
3. Do you believe that conventional dieting is the best or only way to lose weight? Give your reasons.

3

Weights and Measures

It is morning and time for the ritual weigh. You time it carefully to maximise your results. It has to be after you've emptied your bladder (after a night's sleep that could make a difference of a pound, at least!) and it should, of course, be before having the early morning cuppa. It is best to remove all clothing to get the true picture (no matter how gruesome it appears), and who knows, maybe you should cut your fingernails and shave your legs! If the scales don't pat you on the back, then you can always try moving them around the room. (I found that my digital scales gave a lower reading when placed on the bath rug than they did on the tiled floor!)

Does all this sound excessive? Of course it is. Yet this was, to a point, the way I operated while on a diet, and a good number of my readers will smile and identify with what I used to do.

But after I had that rude awakening in January 2004 I decided that the scales should not be allowed to control my life. In fact I even decided not to make weight loss my main goal. I understood from previous experience that if I just set myself a specific weight target one of two things might easily happen. I would either succeed in reaching my goal and then be tempted to congratulate myself with food, or I would fail, in which case disappointment could lead me into the same undesirable behaviour for reasons of comfort.

Instead of making weight loss my fundamental aim, I felt God was leading me to make good health my goal instead, in which case weight loss would be a means to an end and not an end in itself. After all, there are some thin people who are far from healthy and some fat ones who, in spite of their weight, seem to be in relatively good health. Perhaps even I fell into this category, for in truth I had had no medical problems other than slightly high blood pressure which raised the doctor's eyebrows from time to time. I had also begun to have some pains in my knee joints which probably had to do with the weight I was carrying, but that was all.

Although neither my husband nor I had major health concerns, we were both of an age, in our middle-to-late 50s, whereby we realised that we might well run into trouble if we didn't take preventative action. The risk of contracting many illnesses is shown to be exacerbated by being overweight . . . heart disease, stroke, osteoarthritis, some cancers, sleep apnoea, heartburn, gout and diabetes being the main ones.

As a Christian, I knew my body to be a temple of the Holy Spirit (1 Corinthians 6:13–20) and that as such I should 'glorify God in [my] body' (verse 20). I had sought, over the years, to obey this injunction in all sorts of spiritual and moral ways and yet, curiously, had not applied it in the most straightforward literal way of allowing God to be in control of my food and eating. Now, faced with the evidence given by the scales, I repented, submitted my appetite to God and asked Him to help me lose weight for His glory, as well as for my health's sake.

Although I had escaped any serious consequence of ill health, I was soon to learn just how much at risk I had been, even though I was not experiencing many adverse symptoms. There are three easy tests that all of us can do at home which, together, give a pretty fair assessment of how much our health may be in jeopardy in relation to our weight.

1. Body Mass Index

The first is to discover our Body Mass Index. This takes a person's height and weight and, through applying a mathematical equation, comes up with a numerical score. A score of between 20 and 25 is considered 'normal' while a score of 30-plus is considered obese, and below 18 may be indicative of an eating disorder such as anorexia. The way it is calculated is by taking one's weight in kilograms or pounds, and measuring one's height in metres or feet and inches. The weight is then divided by the square of the height and the answer is the BMI. Sounds complex? Yes, it is a little, but don't worry, a BMI chart is included (see Figure 2 on page 45). Simply take your two measurements and look across the two corresponding axes of the graph to where the points meet, and that will tell you your BMI.

The Body Mass Index on its own however, is an imprecise tool. It cannot differentiate between fat, bone or muscle. Consequently a person who has a larger bone structure will have a higher reading than one who is of a slighter build; and an athlete, with lots of muscle and little fat, may have a higher BMI than someone who is very fat yet has little muscle mass. In fact recent research recorded in *The Lancet* found that, once factors such as smoking and exercise habits were taken into consideration, the BMI had no significant bearing on heart-attack risk.[1] Even more surprising is a report published in *The Journal of the American Medical Association* which stated that, while underweight and obesity (a BMI of 30 or more) were both associated with an increased risk of death, those categorised as 'overweight' (a BMI of 25 to 29.9) were actually at reduced risk of death![2] Something more is needed to complete the picture and this where the waist-to-hip ratio is a good indicator.

2. Waist-to-Hip Ratio (WHR)

There is a growing recognition that it is not overall fat, but specifically fat which accumulates around the abdomen, that is strongly linked with poor health potential. *The Lancet* study found that a higher ratio of waist circumference to hip circumference (waist-to-hip ratio) was very clearly associated with increased heart-attack risk. A ratio of 1.1 is in the danger zone, so the clear message is to make sure that your waist isn't bigger than your hips! Ideally, men and women should have waist-to-hip ratios (expressed as decimals) no larger than about 0.90 and 0.83 respectively and a

---

[1] 'Association of Bodyweight with Total Mortality. . . ', in *The Lancet* (vol. 368, no. 9536)

[2] Briffa, Dr John, 'Hip Service', in *The Observer* magazine (30/11/05)

WHR of less than 0.85 (men) and 0.75 (women) is considered excellent.

To find your WHR, measure your waist (at the smallest area below your rib cage and above your navel) and your hips (at the widest point). Divide your waist measurement by your hip measurement to get your waist-to-hip (decimalised) ratio. If your maths is a little shaky use a calculator!

3. Waist Circumference

An easier, though maybe not so accurate, method for assessing your accumulation of abdominal fat is simply to measure your waist through your naval, not necessarily your narrowest point. For a man a waist measurement over 40 inches (102 cm) is considered dangerous for health, while a measurement less than 37 inches (94 cm) is considered normal. For a woman, anything above 34.5 inches (88 cm) is dangerous, and a measurement below 31.5 inches (80 cm) is normal.

If you are 'apple' shaped – with a tendency to put weight on predominantly around your middle – you are more at risk of contracting heart disease and diabetes than if you are 'pear' shaped, accumulating weight lower down. The latter, however, may present greater problems regarding wear on leg and hip joints and could lead to you developing osteoarthritis.

Bathroom Scales

Being controlled by the scales on a day-to-day basis can be just as destructive and demoralising as being enslaved to a diet. The fact that going on a diet normally necessitates our keeping a regular check on our progress, through the evidence suggested by the bathroom scales, makes losing weight a matter of performance. This can have a negative knock-on effect on our self-esteem, making it that much harder when we do fail to lose weight or remain static, as we inevitably will at times.

Just like the BMI, ordinary bathroom scales cannot distinguish between fat, muscle, water and bone mass – and fat-monitoring scales can be inaccurate. This means that on a day-to-day basis your weight may go up and down, bearing little relationship between that and the food you are consuming. The results can be feelings of depression or of raised false hopes.

Take water retention, which may add several pounds to your weight. This may be due to a number of factors. Perhaps your salt intake went up, in which case your body would retain more fluid. Or, curiously, cutting down on your water consumption may have the same effect, because, as with food, your body, sensing dehydration, holds on to it more. Then, specific to women, is the tendency to retain several pounds of water prior to menstruation, although this increase tends to disappear just as quickly as it arrives a few days later.

Fat, as we have already seen, is bulkier than muscle, but ordinary scales can't tell the difference. If you are seeking to increase your level of physical activity while also trying to lose weight, you may even find that your weight won't alter for a while. This can be very defeating if you look to the scales alone for evidence. Measuring yourself with a tape measure at such times may well indicate that while your weight remains static you are still losing inches and looking sleeker and firmer, which is what you really want.

The scales may also reflect the amount of food you have

just eaten. If you ate a huge dinner, say a couple of pounds, and then weighed yourself immediately afterwards, your weight would register those extra two pounds. But this doesn't mean that you have gained two pounds in weight. Once the food is digested, only that which is surplus to the body's requirement will register as fat.

So even now, if you are embarking upon Fit for Life Forever as a programme to help you regulate your own weight, you may like to consider what you are going to do regarding your scales. If they have been a stumbling block to you in the past, then why not throw them out, or at least hide them for a while. Weigh yourself, first of all, by all means, in order to help assess your overall health risk, but then pay little attention to them until you are beginning to see the results with your own eyes. The mirror and the clothes you wear will tell you all you need to know.

If, like me, you have turned to God for help in regulating your weight, then please understand that you are embarking upon a walk of faith, not sight. Counting calories and weighing food is walking by sight, so too is living your life by the reading on your bathroom scales. These things are not necessarily wrong, but when we walk by faith we look to the Holy Spirit to lead us and bring us in check. Also, since Fit For Life Forever is a non-diet programme it would be inappropriate for you to continue on any diet regime at the same time. It will feel risky at first, because you have grown so used to the external controls, but in time you will come to recognise and value God's direction. I believe you will find such a freedom, not having to live your life under the heavy burden of rules and regulations, that you will soon actually start to enjoy the adventure instead!

Home Assignments

1. Weigh yourself and measure your height. Then use the BMI chart (see Figure 2 below), in order to determine your own Body Mass Index. Work out how much you will need to lose in order to have a BMI in the normal range (18–25).

2. Measure your waist circumference (through your belly button) and then, using the Health Risk chart

Height in feet and inches

Weight in stones and lbs	4'10"	5'0"	5'2"	5'4"	5'6"	5'8"	5'10"	6'0"	6'2"	6'4"
7st 0	20.6	19.2	18.0	16.9	15.9	15.0	14.1	13.3	12.6	12.0
7st 7	22.0	20.6	19.3	18.1	17.0	16.0	15.1	14.3	13.5	12.8
8st 0	23.5	22.0	20.6	19.3	18.1	17.1	16.1	15.2	14.4	13.7
8st 7	25.0	23.3	21.8	20.5	19.3	18.2	17.1	16.2	15.3	14.5
9st 0	26.4	24.7	23.1	21.7	20.4	19.2	18.1	17.2	16.2	15.4
9st 7	27.9	26.1	24.4	22.9	21.5	20.3	19.2	18.1	17.1	16.2
10st 0	29.4	27.4	25.7	24.1	22.7	21.4	20.2	19.1	18.0	17.1
10st 7	30.8	28.8	27.0	25.3	23.8	22.4	21.2	20.0	18.9	18.0
11st 0	32.3	30.2	28.3	26.5	24.9	23.5	22.2	21.0	19.8	18.8
11st 7	33.8	31.6	29.6	27.7	26.1	24.6	23.2	21.9	20.7	19.7
12st 0	35.2	32.9	30.8	28.9	27.2	25.6	24.2	22.9	21.6	20.5
12st 7	36.7	34.3	32.1	30.1	28.3	26.7	25.2	23.8	22.5	21.4
13st 0	38.2	35.7	33.4	31.4	29.5	27.8	26.2	24.8	23.5	22.2
13st 7	39.6	37.0	34.7	32.6	30.6	28.8	27.2	25.7	24.4	23.1
14st 0	41.1	38.4	36.0	33.8	31.7	29.9	28.2	26.7	25.3	23.9
14st 7	42.6	39.8	37.3	35.0	32.9	31.0	29.2	27.6	26.2	24.8
15st 0	44.0	41.2	38.5	36.2	34.0	32.0	30.2	28.6	27.1	25.7
15st 7	45.5	42.5	39.8	37.4	35.2	33.1	31.2	29.5	28.0	26.5
16st 0	47.0	43.9	41.1	38.6	36.3	34.2	32.3	30.5	28.9	27.4
16st 7	48.5	45.3	42.4	39.8	37.4	35.2	33.3	31.4	29.8	28.2
17st 0	49.9	46.6	43.7	41.0	38.6	36.3	34.3	32.4	30.7	29.1
17st 7	51.4	48.0	45.0	42.2	39.7	37.4	35.3	33.3	31.6	29.9
18st 0	52.9	49.4	46.3	43.4	40.8	38.5	36.3	34.3	32.5	30.8
18st 7	54.3	50.8	47.5	44.6	42.0	39.5	37.3	35.3	33.4	31.6
19st 0	55.8	52.1	48.8	45.8	43.1	40.6	38.3	36.2	34.3	32.5
19st 7	57.3	53.5	50.1	47.0	44.2	41.7	39.3	37.2	35.2	33.3
20st 0	58.7	54.9	51.4	48.2	45.4	42.7	40.3	38.1	36.1	34.2
	4'10"	5'0"	5'2"	5'4"	5'6"	5'8"	5'10"	6'0"	6'2"	6'4"

Figure 2 – BMI Chart of Height / Weight Ratios

BMI		Normal waist circumference	Large waist circumference
18 to 20	Underweight	-	N/A
20 to 25	Normal	-	N/A
25 to 30	Overweight	Increased	High
30 to 35	Obese	High	Very high
35 to 40	Obese	Very high	Very high
40+	Extremely obese	Extremely high	Extremely high

Figure 3 – Health Risks of Combined BMI and Waist Measurements

(see Figure 3 above), work out your own level of overall risk. How many inches will you need to lose off your waist in order to be in the normal range of 31.5 to 34.5 inches (women) and 37 to 40 inches (men)? Use a calculator to work out your waist-to-hip ratio.

3. How have you reacted in the past to information given by bathroom scales? Is it going to be helpful for you to weigh yourself frequently or should you think of hiding your scales for a while?

4. How can you walk by faith rather than sight in this matter of weight regulation?

4

Eating – a Holistic Experience

The word 'holistic' is an adjective relating to the noun 'holism' which first came into usage in the 1940s. Although it is a word often used in connection with alternative therapies (many of which Christians might consider suspect) it is nevertheless one which we can use in a correct context without fear of compromising our faith. By general definition 'holistic' simply means: 'a whole made up of interdependent parts'. The most common usage, and that which I am applying here, is in reference to body, mind and spirit.

The Nature of Man

Before we can begin to understand the roots to our eating problems it is necessary to lay some groundwork by discussing the nature of man. A widely held Christian philosophy concerning the nature of man can be neatly summed up as follows: 'Man is a spiritual being. He has a soul and lives in a body.' It is through our body that we come into contact with the material world and thus develop world ousness. The soul expresses man's personality and ..... is what gives him self-consciousness, and the spirit, the noblest part of all, is that part by which man is able to have God-consciousness.

Food Affects Us on All Levels of Our Being

While the primary relationship between ourselves and food lies at the physical level – our bodily structure being renewed and maintained through the nutrients found in food – our relationship with food affects us at every level of our being. In this chapter we shall be looking at the sensory aspects of the physical and also those areas of the soul which relate to our mind and will. Our emotional responses to food and eating are so vast as to constitute several chapters on their own, while the spiritual is dealt with in depth in Chapter 7, entitled 'The Spiritual Void'.

The Physical Level

The importance of the body is that it is the vehicle for the expression of our soul and spirit and as such should be cherished and maintained in good health so far as is possible. The physical aspects of our make-up, relevant to food and eating, are the digestive system, our hormonal system and the five senses. Various aspects of digestion and hormones have already been discussed in relation to dieting and we will speak of them further as they relate to other matters. So for now we will look at the third aspect, that is *our senses,* every one of them – sight, hearing, smell, touch and taste – being used to heighten (or diminish) our whole eating experience and stimulate our appetite.

Appetite is defined by some as being different from hunger. Hunger, it is said, relates to physiological need, while appetite relates more to non-physiological desire. Although my own dictionary research fails to support this distinction, it is useful to our topic to make it nevertheless. Therefore, with these refinements in mind, we could say that when we are *hungry* our *appetite* will arouse our senses in a specific direction so that we not only eat what our body needs to function but also what we feel will satisfy us the most.

Take *sight*. Who can deny the powerful suggestive effect of seeing an image of delicious food, presented attractively before our eyes? The food advertisers use this to maximum effect and bombard us endlessly with their pictures in magazines, on TV and on the cinema screen. Apparently up to 200 images of food can be flashed before us within just one hour of evening TV viewing! Before it was made illegal, food companies could even insert the odd frame carrying an image of food into a movie, which came and went so quickly that it never registered with our consciousness at all. This is called 'subliminal advertising' and the brief exposure had the power to imprint a product on the viewer's mind prompting a desire for that same product, which was, of course, readily available during the interval!

Think about how often you have eaten something simply because you saw it, it was available and you fancied it. This is why supermarkets place sweet confectionary near the checkouts. It can be hard to resist when it is right before your eyes as you patiently wait in line to be served.

Then there is the sense of *smell*. The aroma of a food can be responsible for up to 90% of its flavour. When we drink, suck or chew, volatile gases are released from the food which flow out of the mouth and up the nostrils to a thin layer of nerve cells called the olfactory. These (combined with taste) help us decide whether the food is pleasant to eat or not. Some of the most alluring smells regarding food, for many Western people, are those of freshly baked bread and cooking bacon, but it can be anything at all. Smells, of course can have the opposite effect, and the revulsion that some people feel, especially children, towards vegetables such as cabbage and cauliflower, can be attributed largely to their strong, pungent odours.

What about the sense of *hearing*? This is less powerful, because food often has no associated sounds. But the sound of sizzling bacon or sausages, combined with the smell, can be very hard to resist. What about the crunching sound as we bite into potato crisps or an apple, or the 'snap, crackle, pop' of a certain breakfast cereal? And some researchers even believe that the crunching sound which accompanies the eating of crisps, combined with their salty, fatty taste, has a therapeutic effect on the eater.

The sense of *touch* brings us to the question of texture, which is another important, though less obvious, stimulant to our appetite. For instance, advertisers will often refer to the 'smoothness' of chocolate in their sales pitch. Cakes may be sold by highlighting their 'lightness' or salad by its 'crispness'. The texture of food can also be a turn-off. Some of you may be old enough to remember tapioca pudding being served up for school dinners. I hated it simply because of the sticky, globular feel as it descended my gullet. It really did remind me of frogspawn!

Touch is also the last line of defence when we are fighting

temptation. We may be bombarded with all the sights and smells of succulent, delicious food, but once we've reached out our hands (or forks) and made contact, then it is just about a lost cause. Strong indeed is the person who can pick up that tempting bar of chocolate and put it back down. If you were good at doing that then you probably wouldn't need to read this book!

Last, but certainly not least, is the sense of *taste*. The tastebuds on the tongue can identify the presence of six basic tastes: sweet, sour, bitter, salty, astringent and 'umami' (that triggered by the amino acids in foods such as shellfish, mushrooms and potatoes). We are, by all accounts, born with a natural liking for sweet foods, but our tastebuds can actually be trained, by repeated exposure, to like anything. Besides sugar, the two foods which augment the taste of otherwise bland foods are salt and fat. Since excesses of all three of these foods are deemed bad for our health, it is no wonder that 'diet food', largely depleted of such ingredients, may have little or no appeal to many of us. Food producers, in their attempts to cash in on whatever the latest trend might be – 'low fat', 'low sugar', 'low salt' – have to increase the one ingredient in order to reduce the other; otherwise processed food would be tasteless!

If touch represents the last line of defence then, for many, taste means total surrender! Once the mouth is in gear there really is no stopping it! One half of the Easter egg isn't enough, we must eat it all; a handful of crisps is never enough, we must consume the whole bag. And yet, curiously, once we are on this treadmill, it can be that after the first few mouthfuls we become oblivious to the taste. We eat, as it were, on autopilot, in a mesmerised kind of way, only to resume consciousness when we reach our hand into the bag and there is nothing left!

When the Sensual Becomes Sin

Our five senses are undeniably crucial to our enjoyment of food, but when we give in to their demands it can lead us into two types of excessive, sinful behaviour. The first is *lust*, a term relating not only to sexual misdemeanour, but to any God-given drive taken to excess. In the same way that sexual lust is excited through the sense of sight (as in pornography, for instance), so too lust for food springs into action by visual stimulation or mental imaging. It isn't driven by real, legitimate need, as in physiological hunger, but simply by seeing, imagining and desiring due to the arousal effect of the senses:

> Let no one say when he is tempted, 'I am tempted by God': for God cannot be tempted by evil nor does he himself tempt anyone. But each one is tempted when he is drawn away by his own desires and enticed. Then when desire is conceived, it gives birth to sin; and sin, when it is full-grown, brings forth death. (James 1:13–15, NKJV)

It is the nature of sin to pass the blame. But when we are drawn away by our own desires, we are solely responsible for the subsequent choices we make.

The second besetting sin which relates to food is *gluttony*, which is the name given to greed specifically in the area of food. If lust can be expressed as, 'I see therefore I desire', gluttony is expressed as, 'there is more available so I must have'. Our parents had an expression for it: 'Your eyes are bigger than your belly', only we have abused our bellies for so long that they have expanded to accommodate our excessive demands and can no longer exercise any restraint on our runaway appetites. It is gluttony which is in operation when we pile up our plates at a buffet-style restaurant or automatically go for seconds even when we have had to slacken our belts. It is gluttony in operation when we accept the offer of 'going large' at a fast-food restaurant, simply because we've rationalised that it is good value for money. And it is corporate, nationally sanctioned gluttony that persuades us to cast off all restraint for the whole of the Christmas holiday period and go on a binge for anything up to ten days – maybe even longer. I once had a meal with a rather rotund elder of a French church. As he gorged his way through the several courses, always accepting offers of second helpings, he made this comment: 'Gluttony isn't a sin – it is simply an appreciation of what is good!' Perhaps we can have too much of a good thing.

It is not, however, the purpose of this book to send my readers on a guilt trip. You've had enough of those, through dieting, to last a lifetime. But if you are in real earnest about changing your eating lifestyle, then you are going to have to be deadly honest with yourself and 'call a spade a spade'. Perhaps you have hidden unintentionally from yourself by using statements such as, 'I just love my food', when what you really mean is that you lust after it or are a glutton.

'Ouch! That hurt!' I can almost sense you wincing. But I'm not giving you any stronger medicine than I've had to administer to myself. You see, I came to understand that when I said things like, 'I just love food', I was mentally disguising my vice as a virtue, and all the time that I was living in this deception God couldn't help me and I remained in captivity.

But Jesus said, 'You will know the truth and the truth will set you free' (John 8:32). Truth cannot set us free until we know it and that involves owning it. It is only our human pride and shame that causes us to hide from our own condition, but when we humble ourselves to accept the truth, then God's grace is there in abundance to rescue us and forgive.

In 1 Corinthians 10:13 we read: 'God is faithful who will not allow you to be tempted beyond what you are able, but with the temptation will also make the way of escape that you may be able to bear it' (NKJV). This is a wonderful Scripture promise, which we can apply to any number of situations where we are tempted to do what isn't right or helpful. Temptation begins by capturing our attention, so sometimes *our way of escape* is simply to focus our attention on something else. Rick Warren says: 'When temptation calls you on the phone, don't argue with it, just hang up!'[1]

Whenever possible we would be wise to take the route of avoidance, physically leaving a tempting situation. 'This is one time when it is okay to run away. To avoid being stung, stay away from bees.'[2] So if, for instance, you habitually pass by a confectioner's shop on the way to work and can't resist what you see in the window, then a practical strategy would be for you to take an alternative route, thus avoiding the temptation. Or if it is hard for you to resist eating a certain snack food when it is readily available in the house,

---

[1] Warren, Rick, *The Purpose-driven Life* (Zondervan, 2002)
[2] Ibid.

then, knowing your weakness, it is probably best to make the personal decision not to buy it in, at least until you have grown sufficiently in your faith and understanding to be able to manage things better.

But note that God's way of escape isn't necessarily the way of avoidance. He says that He will make a way of escape so that we can *bear* it. God does not always remove the temptation from us, or us from the temptation. Rather He rescues us in the midst of the temptation, because He is our way of escape. 'The Name of the Lord is a strong tower. The righteous run to it and are safe' (Proverbs 18:10, NKJV). It is as we call upon His name, crying out for God to help us, that He comes through powerfully on our behalf, enabling us to stand victorious in His strength, not our own.

The Mind and Food

In our struggles against overeating, food isn't really our enemy – it is our thoughts. In Proverbs 23:7 it says that as a man thinks in his heart, so is he. What a person believes really does rule them and, within the scope of things concerning our relationship with food and eating, there are a number of aspects to consider.

Eating Etiquette

Many of our cultural ideas about food and eating stem back to early childhood. Do we ever seek to question their validity, I wonder? Take, for instance, the compulsion many of us have felt to eat up everything on our plate, even when we feel absolutely stuffed. Even in our own homes, where no one is likely to be offended, this can be one of the hardest things to do, especially if the food isn't something that can be easily stored as 'leftovers' for another day. For some people, the thought of putting anything in the bin would send them on such a guilt trip as to make it not worth contemplating. It's as if a record starts to play somewhere in our subconscious telling us to 'think about the starving millions' in Africa or China. (Incidentally I've discovered that parents tell their children this in places as diverse as the Philippines and Mauritius!) There isn't a thread of logic linking a hypothetical global famine situation with the food we happen to leave on our own plate at any given time, but the guilt association can be strong. And so we become human dustbins, abusing our bodies without giving our spurious logic a second thought. In seeking to avoid the food going to 'waste', we allow it instead to go to our 'waist'!

Then there is the 'three-square-meals-a-day' mantra. This probably has its origins way back in history when the majority of folk were involved in farming and had to engage in hard manual labour from dawn to sunset. Under such circumstances three square meals a day were undoubtedly necessary to keep the body well fuelled. But today most of us lead a far more sedentary lifestyle. We travel by car to work rather than walk; we sit at desks all day rather than work manually; we drive to the shops and have only to carry things from the car to the house; and we are entertained passively by the TV in the evenings. Under these circumstances three square meals a day can be a recipe for disaster – it is far more food than many of us really need.

Meal 'Times'

Many of us eat 'by the clock' rather than listening to our bodies to determine whether or not we are hungry. I asked someone just the other day if she was ready to eat yet. Her answer was to look at her watch and say, 'Well, it's half past five.' I replied to this by saying that I hadn't wished to know the time; I wanted to know if she was ready to eat! How often we sit down to food simply because it's a certain hour of the day and we've always eaten at that time. We have become somewhat like Pavlov's dogs, salivating as a conditioned response to the sound of a bell, only instead of a bell it's the reading on our watches which determines our behaviour. Combine this mentality with the 'clean plate club' and the body can easily be in overload.

Rationalisations

Many of our reasons for eating when we don't need to are plainly unreasonable when viewed objectively, but we convince ourselves of their validity by a process of rationalisation. *The Oxford Modern English Dictionary* defines 'rationalise' in this way: 'to offer or subconsciously adopt a rational (logical) but specious (superficially feasible but actually wrong) explanation of one's behaviour or attitude.'[3] Basically it is just an excuse – a lie with a skin of a reason! However, the persuasive power of rationalisation, especially to ourselves, will cause us to agree concerning our need to eat inappropriately and result in behaviour which simply piles on the pounds. Let's take a look at some of these.

---

[3] *The Oxford Modern English Dictionary* (Oxford University Press, 1995)

'They Made Me Do It'

Someone else made the suggestion to have gateau with the coffee and, although you say that you didn't really want it, you had some just to keep the other company. Well, that's a neat way of turning a vice into a virtue, isn't it? Let's face it: you wanted the gateau all along. You were a pushover!

In my own household there was a time when this kind of thinking really had a strong negative effect on my own eating habits. My husband's guilt reliever, so far as food was concerned, was to co-opt me into eating as well. 'Do you fancy a custard slice?' he'd ask, as we walked past a bakery. 'No, it's alright,' I would answer, secretly wanting one but wishing to appear virtuous. 'You have one, though.' I could afford to say this because I knew only too well how the well-rehearsed script would continue. 'No, it's okay. If you're not having one, I won't bother.' You can probably guess what came next: 'Oh, go on then, I'll have one, but just to keep you company.' All the time that I held to the belief that I was doing this for him, in a selfless kind of way, I avoided the guilt of eating what I didn't need. And all the time I shared in my husband's mini-binge, he somehow felt absolved from feeling too guilty as well, after all, 'A guilt shared is a guilt halved.' (Actually it's a guilt doubled – but that's another rationalisation!)

'Just in Case' Eating

You're going somewhere and are not sure when you'll next be able to eat, so you decide to stock up while you can. This kind of rationalisation presents itself as doing what is 'sensible'; in fact you can congratulate yourself for positively taking care of your body. However, when it turns out that there is ample food available where you're going, or that you were not gone for more than a couple of hours anyway (so no mealtime was actually missed) do you take that into account and cut down accordingly? Of course not! Some other rationalisation takes over providing you with all the reasons you need to eat again.

A variation on this 'just in case' scenario is when you are preparing to do something quite physical, like go to the gym: 'I'm going to need my stamina, so I'd better have something to eat *in case* I start to feel faint,' you reason. You never have felt faint when doing exercise, but who knows? Better to be safe than sorry. And of course, after exercising you are going to need to build up your energy again to make up for all that you've expended. I think you know what comes next!

Value for Money

I've already mentioned the 'value for money' logic which was part of my own downfall. This, too, is yet another form of rationalisation. Such reasoning will cause you to overfill your plate at a buffet or eat everything on your plate in a restaurant which offers generous portions. 'I've paid for it, so I'm jolly well going to eat it,' is the kind of thinking we adopt, thus convincing ourselves that we are being economical rather than gluttonous. Incidentally research shows that portion size in restaurants have actually doubled in the last ten years. When fast-food outlets offer to 'supersize' your order for a pittance, it can appear economically sound to go for it. Well, that's the rationalisation, but the real reason may be just plain gluttony.

'It's Free!'

Closely allied to this last point is the thinking that says, 'It's free, so get all you can.' The church social, the dinner party, the sweets or chocolate handed round the room, tasters offered to passers by in the supermarket . . . all these amount to free food. 'Pity to turn it down,' we reason, as if feeling sorry for the food and not wanting it to suffer from rejection! So down it goes. Combine this thinking with the sensory 'I see therefore I want', and the connoisseur mentality that simply must try anything new and it's easy to see what a powerful influence our thoughts can have.

Associative Eating

This is where eating is viewed as part and parcel of another activity. Obvious examples of this are our cultural linking of going to the cinema with eating popcorn, or travelling with buying sweets and chocolate. But people with eating problems often develop strong associative ties unique to themselves. Perhaps it is a link between a particular television programme and a certain food, or maybe the appearance of adverts on the TV signals the need to go into the kitchen and graze. Perhaps you have developed a ritual of visiting a certain coffee shop for a 'café mocha' and cake when going shopping. You view it as a treat, but it's as predictable as the dawn and your shopping expedition wouldn't be the same without it.

Special Events

We also associate *special events* with overeating, especially Christmas or (in America) Thanksgiving. Then there are birthdays and anniversaries which are often celebrated with excessive food. Somehow these special days wouldn't seem complete without pushing the boat out and eating enough to make it sink. And what about holidays? A new environment presents new opportunities to savour the local fare and with only a fortnight to do it in, well, you're bound to put on a few pounds, aren't you? Putting on weight on holiday is the expected norm. It is the time to cast off all restraint and to do and eat whatever you like.

Thoughts About 'Me'

So far we have only examined our thought patterns as they relate to our false and / or unhelpful beliefs about food and eating, but just as powerful, if not more so, are the thoughts that we entertain concerning ourselves. If your mind is full of negative thoughts about yourself, if you have a poor self-image, then this can greatly influence your relationship with food. It has been said: 'You are not what you think you are, but what you think – you are.' These are powerful words. If you continually think of yourself as a failure, for instance, guess what? – you will fail. If you think of yourself as fat and ugly it may become a self-fulfilling prophecy.

There was one powerful yet wrong self-perception which held me back from losing weight over the years. It was this: God made me fat. I had always been overweight, even when I was younger and more athletic; I had tried repeatedly to lose weight and couldn't keep it off; and my family background indicated that obesity was probably in my genes. It helped me emotionally to explain away my failed attempts, but this line of reasoning eventually caused me to just about give up. Had not God delivered me from this lie I would almost certainly have remained obese to this very day. My belief was ruling me.

Once I turned 50 another thought came into play: 'You don't think you're going to lose weight now – not now that you're menopausal!' This way of thinking came partly by hearsay and partly by observation. Many people, both men and women, once they turn 40, do put on weight – a phenomenon we all know as 'middle-age spread'. And so, the older I got, the more convinced I became that I was fighting a lost cause. Well, that is just another unhelpful belief which God had to deliver me from. I haven't met too many women who can say that they weigh less in their 50s than they have ever done in all their adult life, but I am living proof that it can happen. It all started with changing my way of thinking and it can happen to you too.

Eating and Our Will

It is through your will that you exercise choice and, regarding food, you are making choices all the time: basic decisions about what to buy and cook, when to eat and even how our food should be prepared. For instance, will you roast, boil or fry your potatoes? Will you buy tinned fruit in syrup or just in its own juices? Will you purchase a low-fat spread or go for the butter? Should you prepare a dessert or make do with the main course? Will you have toast as well as cereal for breakfast? It is also through the process of choice that you decide whether or not to follow through on the miscellany of thoughts suggested in the previous section. You hear in your head, for instance, the arguments for and against having that second helping of apple crumble, but your will decides the outcome.

Many yo-yo dieters beat themselves up, believing that the root of their problem is a weak will. 'I see food and just cave in,' they admit. 'I try to keep to my diet, but with so much temptation around it's impossible.' And so we add self-condemnation to our poor self-image, making us feel even more wretched. But knowing what you now do about the very nature of diets, it's easy to see how gritting your teeth to try and make a go of it is, at best, a valiant effort against overwhelming odds.

The attack on our will is a three-pronged attack. Firstly, it is the enticement of temptation in the form of delectable food (or any old food in some instances) which has a powerful pull on our senses. Then it is also an attack from our thought-life as already demonstrated, presenting very powerful arguments in favour of eating when we don't really need to. Thirdly, it is an attack through our coping responses to negative emotions, causing us to look to food for comfort and solace (more about this in a moment). Is it any wonder that we find food so hard to resist? Turning to diets to try and solve our problems in the face of all of this is a complete waste of time.

So far we have been addressing the problem of a weak will, but a strong, defiant will is just as much a problem. When we were children we had to do just what our parents told us to do. They had a very powerful controlling influence on our lives, even in the area of food. There were times, perhaps, when we were made to eat what we didn't want, and other times when we were denied what we really did want. This can produce a defiance, as we get older, which uses food as a means of expressing that we are now in control and that no one can tell us what to eat or what not to eat any more. So if a parent, spouse or significant other in our lives comments that we are getting fat and shouldn't we cut back in our eating, our reaction can be to dig our heels in and eat even more. Alternatively, if we have been losing weight, they might make a comment about being too slim and seek to make us eat more, resulting in a rebellious determination to lose even more weight. Nearly all sufferers of anorexia nervosa have control issues in their lives stemming back to childhood, especially where there has been a very controlling mother. The irony of all this is that what begins as a personal attempt to exert control ends up as satanic bondage where one has no control over one's own self-destructive behaviour. A rebellious attitude always opens up the door to Satan.

God's word tells us that the way to overcome sin and temptation is to walk in the Spirit. 'Walk by the Spirit,' we read in Galatians 5:16, 'and you will not gratify the desires of the flesh.' Victory over our unhelpful, self-destructive eating habits is not only possible, it is a glorious certainty, if we will fulfil the conditions. Basically, what this means is that we have to surrender our wills to God, for in James 4:7 we read that we should submit to God and then resist the devil, so that he will flee from us. To try and resist the devil without first bringing our lives into total submission to God is quite futile. It is Christ who overcame all the works of the devil and only in Him can we share that victory in our own lives. Jesus gave His disciples power and authority over all demons (Luke 9:1) but we can only appropriate this authority as we abide in Him, which means acknowledging our total dependency on His power within us to bring us success. 'Apart from me, you can do nothing' (John 15:5). How true this is.

Home Assignments

1. Write down three foods you really enjoy and three that you dislike. Describe as fully as you can, in relation to the five senses, why these foods have such appeal or revulsion for you.
2. 'I see therefore I want.' How is this true in your own relationship with food?
3. 'There is more available so I must eat it.' In what ways is this statement true of your own eating behaviour?
4. Throughout the week, seek to be in touch with the thought processes that cause you to be tempted to eat when you are not hungry. You could use the headings given in this chapter and add other reasons of your own.
5. Keep a list of when you are tempted to eat inappropriately. In each situation, what way of escape does God provide for you?
6. Do you generally consider yourself to be strong- or weak-willed where food is concerned? Give your reasons.
7. How is God able to help you to 'walk in the Spirit' so that you do not fulfil the 'lusts of the flesh?'

5

The Feel-good Factor of Food

The birthday party, the job promotion, a win for your home team, the lucrative business deal, a family member returning home . . . how do we celebrate? With food, of course. As we turn now to food and our emotions it is worth remembering that we use food (and alcohol) just as much to reinforce positive emotions as we do to alleviate negative ones.

Feel-good Foods

There are certain foods that can be termed 'feel-good' foods. These contain a substance called tryptophan, which produces the naturally occurring, neuro-chemical serotonin in the brain. Serotonin is one of the most important brain chemicals for regulating mood, and if levels are extreme then emotional states as diverse as hyperactivity and depression can result. There are many foods containing tryptophan. Some only produce a short-lived effect, like biscuits and chocolate, caffeine, refined carbohydrates such as crisps and other processed foods and alcohol. But many healthier foods also contain the chemical: there are significant amounts of tryptophan in chicken, turkey, fish, bananas, pineapples, plums, eggs, nuts, avocados, cheese, cottage cheese, milk, beans, peas and soya, while smaller amounts are found in bread, potatoes, rice and cereals.

Few would disagree that God intends for eating to be a positive emotional experience, for He 'richly provides us with everything to enjoy' (1 Timothy 6:17). Enjoyment is an emotion, which, in relation to food, is derived from the rich variety of tastes, colours, smells and textures He has created. Not only this, but He has created us as unique individuals, with our own preferences, likes and dislikes. But many people struggling with weight issues have actually lost their joy and pleasure of eating. It isn't that food has ceased to taste good, but that what is pleasurable to the senses has been found to have a nasty sting in its tail – it adds to our misery by piling on the pounds. And so it is that many have developed a kind of love-hate relationship with food, momentarily savouring the taste and the sense of comfort it brings, yet being filled with guilt, shame and remorse as soon as the food has been eaten.

Emotional Eating

As we have already seen, we humans eat for many reasons. Eating which is associated with and triggered by emotional drives rather than true physiological hunger can be described as 'emotional eating'. It is important for our success in weight regulation and our general wellbeing that we learn to discern the difference.

Here are some clues that you can use to help you know

whether you are eating out of hunger or to fulfil an emotional need:

- Physical hunger comes on gradually whereas emotional hunger tends to appear suddenly.
- Physical hunger can wait a while to be satisfied, but emotional hunger comes with an intensity which demands immediate gratification.
- Once physical hunger is satisfied it is relatively easy to stop eating, but emotional hunger is never satisfied and you continue to eat even when you know you are full.
- Emotional hunger is often associated with specific food cravings to suit specific moods. This will vary according to the individual.
- Because emotional eating is out of control it leaves us feeling powerless, guilty and ashamed.

Up to 70% of the population admit to overeating due to emotional factors at least once a month.[1] This includes boredom, loneliness, anxiety, fatigue, sadness, anger, depression, guilt, shame and stress, but it can also include happy emotions, the food being used to help maintain that mood. Of course, not everyone responds to their emotions by turning to food; some people even experience the opposite effect of being unable to face food when their emotions are disturbed.

Emotional eaters tend also to turn to specific kinds of food, most of which are calorie-rich and high in fat and

---

[1] 'What is Compulsive Eating Behaviour?', on The Cedric Centre for Counselling website: www.compulsiveeating.com/compulsive_eating.htm (accessed 10/12/06)

sugar. According to an article by Brian Wansink, PhD, the director of the Food and Brand Lab at the University of Illinois, in the July 2000 *American Demographic Journal*:

> The types of comfort foods a person is drawn toward varies depending on their mood. People in happy moods prefer. . . foods such as pizza or steak (32%). Sad people reached for ice cream and cookies 39% of the time and 36% of bored people opened up a bag of potato chips.

How does your mood affect your choice of food, I wonder? Not surprisingly, whatever choice of comfort food you may choose, there is a knock-on effect of weight gain, which only serves to increase your feelings of guilt and shame, thus creating a vicious circle in which weight can so easily spiral out of control.

We need only look back to our infancy to discover a possible source of this relationship. As newborn babies our needs were very basic and straightforward. These were: food (in the form of milk), comfort and safety. All of these needs were met in our mother's arms, cradled against her breast, especially so if we were breastfed. Not surprisingly, we formed a very early association in our minds between these three needs, and this is an association which continues, for many, into adulthood. Whenever our emotional needs are inadequately met, for various reasons, we turn to food.

Food helps us emotionally in two powerful ways. Firstly it appears to alleviate and compensate for the pain of negative experiences as they arise, and secondly it helps us keep the pain of past hurtful experiences buried. In short, food helps us to cope. Dr David Ford, a retired GP who works alongside me delivering the Fit For Life Forever course, has observed that throughout his time in general practice almost every case of obesity he came across was linked in some way to emotional issues. Taking pills, stapling the stomach, or going on a diet may have some success in the short term, but these methods never touch on the main issues and cannot provide a long-term cure. For the person who uses food for comfort it is absolutely vital to address the inner emotional needs. Once these are resolved, healing starts to take place from the inside out and is eventually reflected in the restoration of the body to its God-given shape and size.

Disordered Eating

Disordered eating is not the same thing as an eating disorder. The latter is a diagnosed medical condition such as anorexia nervosa, bulimia or binge eating. According to the Eating Disorders Association (EDA) there are around 90,000 people in the UK who are currently diagnosed with these and other eating disorders, but 'in reality the number of people affected is likely to be nearer 1.1 million'.[2] No one, however, has become ill with an eating disorder without having first been on a diet, so the number of people displaying the more general symptoms of disordered eating will be much, much higher.

The main characteristics of disordered eating are:

• A preoccupation with concerns about food, eating and body image.

---

[2] 'Eating Disorder Statistics' in the report 'The Need for Action', on the EDA website, www.edauk.com (accessed 28/11/06)

- An obsession with calorie counting and the numbers on scales.
- Eating compulsively when not really hungry.
- Using food to help cope with difficult feelings.
- Where the need to control food input is a major concern.
- Where (in spite of the above) food controls a person rather than vice versa.
- Feelings of shame, disgust or guilt after eating.
- Compulsive exercising.

Which of the above characteristics apply to you? Perhaps it is just one, or maybe they all apply to some degree. One thing, however, is sure – none of the above symptoms can be 'cured' by going on a conventional diet.

Stress

An overarching term which we use to describe the causes of negative emotions is 'stress'. According to Dr Archibald Hart, stress can result from anything that annoys you, threatens you, prods you, excites you, scares you, worries you, hurries you, angers you, frustrates you, challenges you, criticises you or reduces your self-esteem.[3] There are many causes of stress in life including:

- Death of a spouse, family member or friend.
- Health, including injury, illness or pregnancy.
- Crime: sexual molestation, mugging, theft, etc.
- Self-abuse: drug abuse, alcoholism, self-harm, overeating.
- Family change: separation, divorce, a new baby, marriage.

---

[3] Hart, Archibald, *Adrenaline and Stress* (W Publishing Group, 1985)

- Sexual problems: including getting a partner or with your present partner.
- Arguments: with spouse, family, friends, work colleagues.
- Physical changes: lack of sleep, new work hours.
- New location: vacation or moving house.
- Money: lack of it, owing it or investing it.
- Environment change: in school, job, house, town, prison.
- Responsibility increase: maybe a new dependent or a new job.
- Challenge to perform well: driving test, academic exams, slimming club.

Dieting and Stress

Dieting is in itself stressful for many people, especially when it is undertaken with a specific deadline in view, such as the summer beach holiday or a job interview. The closer one gets to the deadline, so the greater the stress, especially if the weight isn't coming off as quickly as you hoped. A crash diet may seem like the best option, but this is always counter-productive: medical studies have shown that dieting which involves a drastic cut in the intake of calories (especially where there is a heavy restriction on the intake of fats) actually promotes stress, anxiety and depression.

Attending a slimming club can also be stressful because such an emphasis is placed on performance. One abhorrent technique used sometimes is to shame a person when they have gained weight, the aim being to produce a change of behaviour through what is called 'negative reinforcement'. If this approach does bring any behavioural change, it is for all the wrong reasons and cannot produce any lasting beneficial results.

If you have survived the communal weigh-in and the scales confirm what you had hoped – that you've lost a couple of pounds – the built-up stress you had prior to going now begs to be relieved. So what happens? Your thoughts turn to what you can eat by way of a treat; something to reward yourself for all your hard work. And so you make immediately for the very foods that you have been denying yourself all week, reasoning that you have a whole week ahead of you before you have to get weighed again, by which time you hope to have more than compensated for the evening's extravagance. Please, please, if this is you, throw your scales away and don't attend communal weigh-ins where such an emphasis is laid on performance. If you turn to food to reward yourself on a good week, you probably turn to food to find consolation on a bad one. Wise up!

Diets make you preoccupied with food; they keep you feeling hungry and deprived, which may lead to compulsive eating behaviour; they do not address or take away inner pain; they attempt to 'manage' your life, giving you even less control; they focus your attention on food types, making the foods you really enjoy into 'enemies'; and they make your life miserable. Stress is the inevitable outcome. If food were really the issue, then maybe diets would be the answer. But many of our problems in relation to weight have little or nothing to do with food. They go much deeper than that.

How Our Bodies Cope With Stress

We have already spoken of the neuro-chemicals known as 'happy messengers', which are produced in the hypothalamus area of the brain, the chief of which is serotonin. During times of stress, however, they begin to malfunction causing our nerve centres to receive overstress messengers characterised in our bodies by the familiar symptoms of aching, depression, fatigue, insomnia, anxiety and a general feeling of being overwhelmed.

When our bodies experience acute stress, certain stress hormones called glucocorticoids are released which interact with the brain and central nervous system. As the level of these stress hormones increases (the chief of which is cortisol), it leads both to a redistribution of fats within the abdominal area and also to the triggering of various coping mechanisms within the body, one of which is eating, with a preference for high fat, salty or sugary foods. Eating such high-calorie food generates stress-relieving signals in the brain, so we feel better but it will also increase abdominal fat storage.

However, the story does not end here: this accumulation of abdominal fat has also been shown to affect our body's sensitivity to insulin, making it more resistant and therefore less efficient at processing blood glucose. This is a contributory factor in the development and control of adult onset type II diabetes. However, not only does abdominal weight gain lead to insulin resistance, but insulin resistance may itself lead to weight gain – it is yet another vicious circle. Stress contributes to both of these conditions, so it is therefore a very important element in the whole emotional eating scenario.

There is much scientific research going on at the present, which seeks not only to establish the relationship between obesity and stress but also to understand how it operates. Dr

Ulrich-Lai and a team of researchers from the department of psychiatry at the University of Cincinnati found that, when laboratory rats chose to eat or drink sweet snacks, their bodies produced lower levels of cortisol, but the sugar-substitute snacks did not have the same physical effect of lowering both psychological and physical stress.[4] If this is true of humans, then seeking to control stress by eating alternative foods to those high in calories, just won't touch the spot!

Paul Rosch, MD, FACP, the clinical professor of medicine and psychiatry at New York Medical College and president of the American Institute of Stress, has been studying the physical effects of stress in relation to age and sex.[5] He maintains that men and apple-shaped women are both more apt to accumulate deep belly fat and to develop meta-bolically related disorders. He cites research carried out in Sweden in 2003 which found that men with the highest levels of chronic stress also had the highest cortisol meas-urements and the greatest amount of deep belly fat. It is also thought that abdominal fat contains more cortisol receptors than elsewhere in the body, so there is a reciprocal effect: cortisol leading to obesity and abdominal obesity leading to the secretion of more cortisol. Obesity due to stress seems less likely to occur in younger people since their higher lev-els of oestrogen, testosterone and progesterone protect them; but after the age of 40, when these hormones begin

---

[4] Ulrich-Lai, Yvonne, quoted in Kimmon, Dana, 'Sweet Snacks Could be the Best Medicine For Stress', *Medical News Today* (09/01/06)

[5] Rosch, Paul, 'All Obesity is not Created Equal', in *Science* maga-zine (vol. 301, no. 5638, p. 1325, 05/09/03)

to decline, that is when the glucocorticoid levels seem to increase, especially in stressed individuals. Could this be a logical explanation of 'middle-aged spread' in some people?

While the body of medical research seems to indicate a strong and growing correlation between our body chemistry and our emotional state, there is, as yet, no implication that certain people are *genetically* determined to choose food as their particular coping mechanism for stress. It seems more likely that this is a learned, conditioned response; so in your early years, when eating habits were being established, if food was often offered to 'make you feel better', then it is quite likely that you have simply continued the habit into adulthood. Eric Schlosser in his book, *Fast Food Nation*, writes: 'The flavours of childhood food seem to leave an indelible mark and adults often return to them without always knowing why. These "comfort foods" become a source of pleasure and reassurance. . . '[6] It could be, for you, that eating has become your automatic response to reduce bodily stress. Or it may be that you just discovered for yourself that eating soothed your pain. Either way, to try and take this prop away from you now is like trying to take an old bone away from a dog – it merely enhances the need to hold on tight! However, if a juicier bone is offered to the dog, what will he do? He will let go of the old bone without any trouble.

If you are an emotional eater, you clearly need to be freed from you physical dependency on comfort foods as a means of coping with stress. If this response mechanism to stress is

---

[6] Schlosser, Eric, *Fast Food Nation* (Allen Lane The Penguin Press, 2001)

something you learnt, then surely it is something you can unlearn! But to do this you will need to find a 'juicier bone', which is to say, an alternative coping mechanism. Is this possible?

Coping With Stress Without Resorting to Food

There are many, many ways put forward to help people cope with stress – physical, mental and spiritual. Some ways will suit one person and some another. As I put forward some of these ideas now, I suggest that you experiment and find what works best for you. Don't just try and stop yourself comfort eating when you are stressed out, as this will merely increase your anxiety, but have an alternative course of action in mind. Pray and ask the Holy Spirit to guide you.

1. Breathing exercises. Deep, controlled breathing (about ten times) will help you to feel better and more relaxed. When doing such exercises, you should keep your spine straight and maintain a relaxed, comfortable posture.

2. Physical exercise. Physical activity is not only a proven way of increasing the body's metabolism and burning off those extra calories, it is also an excellent way of relieving stress. Here are the many ways in which it works for our benefit:

a) *Exercise helps relieve our adrenaline load.* Stress releases adrenaline into our blood stream causing an additional flow of blood into our heart and our heart rate to increase. Physical exercise helps to relieve this adrenaline overload.

b) *An outlet for anger.* Physical activity can help relieve negative emotions such as anger and hostility, which are associated with stress.

c) *Calms the mind.* Certain forms of repetitive exercise like jogging, cycling and swimming can calm your mind. The consistent breathing and motion associated with such exercises can result in a feeling of calmness and tranquillity.

d) *Enhanced feeling of self-esteem.* This is achieved by knowing that you are accomplishing a health-enhancing experience that is of personal benefit; improving your physical appearance, increasing your self-worth (when valued as part of a team engaged in team sports); and providing challenges which, when conquered, make you feel good about yourself.

e) *Creating personal space.* Exercise can provide a much-needed time of escape from the pressures and demands of daily life, allowing time for introspection.

f) *Endorphin production.* There is some clinical evidence to indicate that the body increases the production of endorphins after 20 minutes or more of exercise. These endorphins can have a pain-relieving effect and can promote a positive mental state which effectively reduces depression and stress-related problems.

g) *Improved sleep.* Interrupted sleep patterns only serve to increase our stress levels and inability to cope. Regular physical activity reduces restlessness associated with stress and encourages a sound sleep.

3. *Soft music* may relax your jarred nerves and bring a sense of calm and equilibrium.

4. *Go to bed on time and get up early*, so you can start the day unrushed. Dr Pamela Peeke, an assistant professor of medicine at the University of Maryland found a direct correlation between sleep deprivation and excessive eating.[7] She says, '90% of the women I see would lose weight if they got a few more hours' sleep a night.' It's certainly worth thinking about.

5. *Try to delegate tasks* to others to reduce your workload.

6. *Learn to pace yourself*, so that you won't feel pressured and are able to give yourself time to face the various challenges in your life. Don't do everything at the last minute. Say 'no' to activities that are just too much or may adversely affect your health.

7. *Live within your budget.* So much stress is financially related.

8. *Get organised* so that you know where things are when you need them. Have extra keys left with friends in case you lose or forget one; buy in extra commodities, such as stamps and toilet rolls so that they are at hand when you run out!

9. *Learn to laugh.* It really is the best medicine and a great stress reliever. Try not to take yourself too seriously. Humour says, 'I'm not alright, and you're not alright – but that's alright!'

---

[7] Peeke, Dr Pamela, *Fight Fat After Forty* (Penguin Non-Classics, 2001)

10. *A nice, hot bath!* Use a relaxing bubble bath, buy a bath pillow, light the candles – aaahh!

Prevention is Better Than Cure

'Stress is what you experience when the responsibilities and demands placed on you at work or at home are beyond your ability to cope.'[8] Stress is a negative response to pressure. These pressures come to us in many forms. Sometimes they are imposed from without and we have no control over them, such as when we lose a job or a close relative becomes ill. At other times, we may be directly responsible for the pressures which have come into our lives, because we have chosen specific courses of action, such as volunteering for extra work, when we are already busy.

It is my firm belief that, while God will allow (indeed cause at times) pressure to come into our lives, He will never burden us with more than we can bear (see, for instance, 1 Corinthians 10:13). This line of reasoning leads to two possible outcomes regarding why we are so often stressed out: either 1) We have taken upon ourselves pressures which are not God-appointed; or 2) We are seeking to cope with God-appointed pressures in our own strength. Any spiritual strategy for coping with stress-related eating must come back to these roots.

In the book of Daniel 7:25 we read that one of the devil's tactics is to wear out the saints. Being stressed and feeling worn out go hand in glove. If the devil can cause us to bite

---

8 'Stress and Eating', on the Mayo Foundation for Medical Education and Research website: www.ediets.com (accessed 28/11/06)

off more than we can chew we will soon feel overwhelmed and unable to cope. If he can cause us to turn to food for our relief rather than seeking God's face, so much the better – becoming obese with its associated health risks can greatly reduce our effectiveness in the kingdom of God.

It is absolutely vital, if we are feeling under stress, that we take stock of our lives in order to know what is of God in our busy schedules and what is not. I remember a time when I was in full-time teaching that I was under extreme stress. Not only did I have a management responsibility within my school and a regular class to teach, but I was also the music co-ordinator and had started five lunchtime music clubs. Added to this, outside of my school responsibilities, I was involved in Bible teaching and leading the worship group in my local church. I was exhausted and one of the ways this manifested itself was through bingeing the minute I walked through the door when I got home! Something had to give, but what?

Obviously, as a paid professional, my first priority was to fulfil the terms of my contract, but I had a spiritual call on my life which I didn't want to neglect either. I loved my musical activities and didn't want to let the children down by stopping the clubs, but this aspect of my work was voluntary. As I prayed about my commitments I saw that the thing which gave me the least job satisfaction was my management responsibility, but to give this up was financially difficult. Finally I decided to take a step of faith: I would give up this position and trust God to meet the shortfall. When I spoke to the head teacher regarding this proposition, she not only accepted my request but drew attention to all the hard work I had been doing regarding music in the school and offered to give me extra money for running the clubs! I only lost half of my extra allowance, was freed from a stack of extra work and pressure, and I was able to enjoy all that God had given me to do without being under too much stress.

If you are stressed out (and overeating) because of work overload, then you need to take a long hard look at your commitments, the way that I did. If you can remove the source of the stress, then the need to comfort eat will take care of itself. Ask yourself why you have taken on certain commitments. Are you perhaps afraid to say no? If so, why is this? Do you have a need to be needed? Are you afraid of rejection if you refuse? To go further into these matters is beyond the remit of this book, but if it strikes a chord within you then please seek counsel from your spiritual mentors. Perhaps you just happen to be a very talented person and people turn to you with all manner of needs. You would like to give yourself to everything, but is it wise? You may end up like a swamp – covering a lot of ground but going nowhere! Ask God where you should be focusing your gifts and abilities and then be prepared to let go of the other things. You are not indispensable.

But what about when the washing machine breaks down, or the car won't start? What about when your mother falls ill and needs your attention? What about the job redundancy with Christmas looming on the horizon and kids who will die of embarrassment at school if they are not given the latest craze in toys or the newest simply-must-have clothing accessory? What if all these things happen together? Such pressures are outside of our control, so it's either sink or swim. Can we really come through times like these without being stressed out?

The best (and most obvious) spiritual counsel anyone can give to help alleviate stress is to pray, but don't you find that this is the last thing you often think of doing when you're in a panic! How many times must God put us through the hoop before we learn? '. . . do not be anxious about anything', Paul exhorts us in Philippians 4:6, 'but in everything by prayer and supplication with thanksgiving let your requests be made known to God.' When we do this then the next verse comes into play. 'And the peace of God, which surpasses all understanding, will guard your hearts and your minds in Christ Jesus.'

When we have a problem God wants us to take it to Him, but this is more than finding a friendly shoulder to cry on so that a 'problem shared is a problem halved'. If all we do is pour out our heart, we may find temporary emotional relief, but we are none the wiser in our understanding of the crisis or what to do. No, we must go a step further, which is – to listen. God wants to speak to us! He wants to shed light on our experience, to grant wisdom, to comfort our hearts; and He cannot do that unless we are still before Him. 'Be still', God says through the psalmist, 'and know that I am God' (Psalm 46:10). He invites us to cease from our striving and to enter into the rest of faith, but we cannot do this if we are running around like headless chickens. If we could only discipline ourselves to run to the Lord, rather than running to the fridge when we are under stress, how different things would be.

There is an optimum level of stress which brings the best out of us, and God knows just where that level is. With Him there is never a last straw to break the camel's back; instead He invites us to take upon ourselves His 'easy yoke', which is really His will. As we bow our heads under this yoke, so that we are walking in step with the Master, our burdens really do become lighter. We have a sense of purpose; we smell the scent of victory; we rise up to the challenge of the moment and see God glorified in our lives and circumstances.

Home Assignments

1. Would you describe yourself as an emotional eater? Give your reasons.
2. Are there any specific foods that you associate with particular moods?
3. Look at the characteristics of disordered eating. Which of these apply to you?
4. Try to identify areas of stress in your life. Are you using food to help you cope with these issues?
5. Choose three ideas from the list, 'Coping With Stress Without Resorting to Food' (see page 77) that you are prepared to try out in your life. Start to practise these.
6. Are you overstretched? If so, review your own regular commitments and prioritise with a view to cutting out some activities. Pray first!
7. 'Be still', says God. Do this, now, for just 15 minutes. Write down what God is showing you. If you found this beneficial do the same thing after reading each chapter.
8. Share what you are learning with a friend. This will reinforce your own learning.

6

Filling the Void

The primary purpose of eating must surely be to fill our empty stomachs, so that our bodies are energised and health is maintained. But we have so often turned to food to try and fill other voids in our lives. From the stories overeaters have related to me I have identified these voids in the following ways:

1. Boredom   –   the activity void
2. Loneliness   –   the relationship void
3. Inner hunger –   the spiritual void

Boredom and loneliness are both the subject of this chapter; inner hunger will be addressed in the next.

Boredom – the Activity Void

C. C. Colton has observed that, 'Ennui [boredom] has made more gamblers than avarice, more drunkards than thirst, and perhaps as many suicides as despair.'[1] Although Colton

---

[1] Colton, C. C., from 'Quotes on Boredom', on the Quote Garden website: www.quotegarden.com/boredom.html (accessed 09/12/06)

does not specifically mention gluttons or overeaters, I firmly believe that boredom is a principle root of much overeating and this has been consistently borne out in all of my own background research.

What causes boredom? There may be some situations in which we are not in control and boredom is simply the predictable outcome of a lack of stimulus – such as having to sit through an uninspiring lecture (or – dare I say it? – sermon). The mind wanders, we doodle on bits of paper, we stare around the room and yawn discreetly, but we do not generally, under such circumstances, eat. Social etiquette would forbid such a thing. No, the situations which result in us reaching for food are usually ones where we are in control and where we *could* choose an altogether different activity to relieve our boredom, if we so wished.

'You'll find boredom where there is an absence of a good idea.'[2] Eating may seem like a good idea at the time, but what a price we pay with our expanding waistlines and excessive weight gain. There must be many better ways to occupy ourselves than this! But what happens? We come in from work, feeling generally exhausted; we do whatever has to be done around the house or prepare an evening meal, and afterwards we plonk ourselves down in front of the TV and seek to be passively entertained. The programmes may be fast moving, colourful, dramatic, full of technical wizardry, but we are bored. We've seen it all before. Even with 600 channels to choose from, we can't

---

[2] Nightingale, Earl, from 'Bores and Boredom', on the Quotations Book website: www.quotationsbook.com/subjects/137/Bores_and_Boredom (accessed 09/12/06)

find what we want. If we've said it once, we've said it a thousand times: 'There isn't anything worth watching.'

Now, from a quality point of view there may be some truth in this, but the problem isn't altogether the fault of the producers. In an interesting study of the use of the word 'boredom' in English literature, author Patricia Spack found a close correlation between the rise of modern technology and the increase in references to boredom in literature and poetry.[3] Another author, Richard Winter, in his book, *Still Bored in a Culture of Entertainment*[4] maintains that over-stimulation caused by technology and exciting entertainment has the capacity to create boredom in us just as much as under-stimulation can. Winter further argues that exciting entertainment actually leads to what he calls 'deadness of soul', a malaise which is deeply spiritual in nature. If boredom is leading you to eat more than you need, could it be that you are experiencing, to some degree, this deadness of soul, even if you are a Christian?

If you identify yourself as a 'boredom eater' then the logical answer is to fill your life with alternatives so that you are no longer bored. But if what these authors I have just cited say is true, then passive entertainment, of any kind, is not the answer. It will merely serve to aggravate your problem. No, what you need is to be engaged in something *active* which will capture your heart and stimulate your mind and imagination. Many people, however, who confess to eating

---

[3] Spack, Patricia, *Boredom: The Literary History of a State of Mind* (University of Chicago Press, 1995)

[4] Winter, Richard, *Still Bored in a Culture of Entertainment* (InterVarsity Press, 2002)

as a result of boredom, seem unwilling to do anything to alter their situation. They have relinquished the responsibility to fill their void to others. They have a victim mentality, never seeming to realise that if their situation is to change then they are the ones who are going to have to make it happen.

People who are bored usually lack commitment to specific goals and plans. If you are a committed Christian then you will surely accept that God has a specific plan and purpose for your life. In Jeremiah 29:11 we read: 'I know the plans I have for you,' declares the Lord, 'plans for wholeness and not for evil, to give you a future and a hope.' Do you know what these plans are? Perhaps you would find it helpful to actually take the time to write down your own long- and short-term goals. Don't just think about spiritual goals, but goals for your own development as a person, goals for your family and goals for your work. Make them as specific as you can. If you do not have any goals or they lack any real definition, then pray and ask the Lord to reveal these things to you. Think about your own gifts and abilities: How could these be developed? How can they be used? What are your dreams and desires? Write them down and then pray about them, asking the Lord to show you how you can begin to make them come to pass.

It may be that He will direct you to a specific course of study or training; or He may want you to join a particular kind of outreach or social action group. Perhaps He is calling you to spend more time alone with Him in prayer. Whatever He shows you, just be obedient. Don't always wait for opportunities to come to you, but begin to be proactive and take steps of faith towards them. Maybe that first step is to talk things through with a spiritual mentor who can pray with you, steer you in the right direction and maintain your accountability. Do not be paralysed through a fear of making mistakes. As long as you are fully submitted to Christ's lordship in your life then you do not need to fear. If you start to pursue something which isn't right for you, the Holy Spirit will soon let you know! For one thing, you will experience a deep-seated uneasiness; but if your spirit is at peace, and your plans are in line with God's word, just go ahead in faith.

Alongside boredom we should also consider the problem of procrastination – putting off until tomorrow what ought to be done today. In this case, it isn't that you don't know what to do, rather you are aware of many things that need to be done, but you can't motivate yourself to do any of them. You'll do the ironing, or decorate the bedroom tomorrow; that 'thank you' letter or missing button can wait until another day; the cupboards could do with a tidy out, but it's too cold or too hot to deal with it right now or you're just too tired. So until you feel more inspired, well, might as well just relax and . . . eat!

Whether your problem is boredom, procrastination or both, I suggest that you start a 'things to do' list in your journal. Jot down anything that comes to mind whether it is mundane or exciting, important or relatively unimportant, urgent or non-urgent. It may be something big like joining an evening art class, or something very small like cleaning out the fridge. Keep on adding to the list whenever you think of something else. Then, when you find yourself reaching for food because you are bored, get the list out and find an alternative activity. Ask God to fill you with passion for what you about to do, even if it is something very ordinary. His word tells us: 'Whatever your hand finds to do, do it with all your might' (Ecclesiastes 9:10). Again we read in 1 Corinthians 10:31: '. . . whatever you do, do all to the glory of God.' Passion has very little to do with the object of our feelings; rather it is a state of mind. Some people are passionate about everything while others are passionate about nothing. It is only 'deadness of soul' that dims your passion and makes everything seem boring. It's time for you to shake the mothballs off your life, to open the windows of your imagination and to get on with real living. When you get actively involved in doing something productive, you will be surprised how quickly thoughts about food and eating (unless you are genuinely hungry) will simply vanish.

Part of God's calling on my own life is to motivate others to enter into God's best for their lives. This book is part and parcel of that commission. But, as the old saying goes, 'You can take a horse to water, but you can't make him drink.' In the end, it's all down to you. If you have identified boredom as a significant factor in your overeating, you know that the answer is to find an alternative activity to fill the void. Now stop making excuses. Get proactive! Make that list, prioritise the tasks that need to be done, and JUST DO THEM!

Loneliness – the Relationship Void

Another thing that technology has done for us besides entertain us to the point of boredom, is to make communications a whole lot easier. Ironically, however, although we are doing a whole lot more communicating in the technical sense, it seems that we are relating to each other far less meaningfully than ever before and this leaves us feeling lonely.

But what exactly is loneliness? It would appear to be one of the most pervasive emotional disorders of all time, but loneliness is more easily experienced than defined. Loneliness does not necessarily mean being alone, for you can feel lonely in a crowd or when you are surrounded by people. No, loneliness is a sense that somehow you are not connected with others and therefore your emotional needs are not being adequately met. It is a painful experience which leaves you feeling unloved, excluded and alienated. It is a feeling that there is no one with whom you can share your own personal concerns and experiences. Solitude may be chosen, but loneliness never is. It is something which you endure either because of your own inability to make meaningful friendships, the lack of opportunity, or both.

Loneliness, unlike boredom, seldom occurs in isolation from other negative feelings. It is often associated with sadness, self-pity and depression. If the loneliness is associated with the break-up of a relationship with some significant other in a person's life it may also be linked to anger, resentment, rejection and the avoidance of further intimacy for fear of suffering more hurt. Where there is a fear of being alone, there may be a sense of abandonment, anxiety and stress.

Loneliness is also closely associated with feelings of low self-esteem and in relation to comfort eating may be the cause, effect or both. If you have low self-esteem you may find it difficult to mix and make friends. Feelings of self-doubt and insecurity may give the impression to others of aloofness when this is not really the case. Filled with false beliefs that nobody likes you, you are nervous to reach out to others for fear of rejection. You become self-conscious and begin to withdraw from social activities; you may avoid meeting people or new situations, but the more you do this, so the more lonely, unhappy and isolated you become. When you are in company, the body signals you send out unwittingly cause others not to come too close, so your fears become a self-fulfilling prophecy.

One way you may have learnt to cope with this is to self-medicate on food. Food is a 'safe' friend: it doesn't say hurtful things or make unreasonable demands; it is forever faithful – there just when you need it; it never rejects you; and most importantly it fills the loneliness void, temporarily at least. But as this dependency grows stronger and stronger, so the toll on your body begins to manifest itself. You become more and more obese and are filled with shame and self-hatred. Your self-esteem continues to plummet and this creates in you an even greater need to comfort eat. The fatter you become, so the more isolated, despairing and depressed you feel.

You do not need to be alone in this world to experience loneliness. You may be in a marriage where you feel ignored or misunderstood, or where your spouse has little regard for your feelings. Or you may feel as though you are living a lie: people like the outgoing sanguine personality you project, but you know that it is not the real 'you'. You are wearing a mask, and although you are outwardly very sociable, inwardly you weep, for there is no one in your life that you feel really connected with. 'If people were to see who I really am,' you reason, 'they certainly wouldn't want me.' Inability to live authentically can be one of the most isolating experiences of all.

Similar to this is the feeling that others only want to be with you because you possess something that others wish to take advantage of. The classic case scenario is that of a rich person who senses that wealth is the only reason why others show any interest. But it need not be money; it may be that you have some special gift or ability, or that you are always willing to do anything others ask of you. But you want to feel that you have significance and value outside of what you have to give; you want to be loved and appreciated for yourself. In your moments of solitude all these negative thoughts and self-doubt begin to surface. The comfort you are looking for lies very close at hand – it is, of course, food.

A recent article in the *Journal of Clinical Nursing*, concerning a joint study by Australian and UK researchers, found that 35% out of 1,289 subjects suffered from loneliness. Unemployed people and those in their 40s ranked highest, but interestingly 'strong belief in religion was found to be a remedy for loneliness'.[5] I do not intend to develop this idea any further right now, as this will be the focus of the next section. Rather, what I wish to do is to suggest various practical ways in which you might find solutions to your dearth of meaningful relationships. I will place a number of keys in your hand, but as in the case of boredom, you are the one who must apply them to the locked door of your circumstances if there is going to be any change.

---

[5] Lauder, W., in *Journal of Clinical Nursing* (March 2006, vol. 15, pp. 334–340)

Dealing With Loneliness

The following ideas may help you if your loneliness is purely circumstantial. If, however, your loneliness stems not from the absence of relationships, but from a low self-esteem and an inability to find true emotional fulfilment, then there are probably deeper inner needs that you need to address. Subsequent chapters of this book may provide you with further insights and offer appropriate help.

1. *Face up to your loneliness.* Find someone you can trust (your pastor or his wife, for instance) and share the ways in which you have identified with the ideas expressed in this section. Ask them to assist you in taking the necessary steps and making connections with others.

2. *Identify social activities which you would like to be involved in.* Seek to find someone who might accompany you on the first few occasions until you feel more confident.

3. *Join groups aimed at helping others.* In this context you are more likely to find others who are compassionate by nature and will therefore be more sensitive to your own needs. It will also help you to take the focus off yourself and your own needs. There is an old poem by Frances Ridley Haver-gal, which reads: 'Seldom can a heart be lonely if it seeks a lonelier still – Self-forgetting, seeking only emptier cups of love to fill.' Visit your local library and find out what voluntary services operate in your area – there are so many to choose from.

4. *Take the initiative.* When in the company of others make

eye contact, smile and introduce yourself. Ask questions which, without appearing nosey, show a genuine interest. Perhaps you could invite a colleague, neighbour or church member round for supper. Alternatively, suggest that you go out for an inexpensive 'two for the price of one' deal at a restaurant. There are probably others in your church who are feeling exactly the way you do. Why not see about organising a singles night? You could put out a short questionnaire to assess interest and find out what others would most like to do.

5. *Take things slowly.* Intimacy is built on trust and this takes time. If you unburden yourself or share intimate things concerning your own life too early you will cause others to back away.

6. *Don't make excuses.* Lonely people often assume that others wouldn't be interested in them or have the time to spare. Single people feel as though they are the odd one out in an environment which is comprised largely of couples and families. This disadvantage may be real enough, but many married individuals quite like to have an evening away from their spouse in order to pursue other friendships (with the same sex, of course!). If you are a female, perhaps some women you know have partners who regularly work late or who have to work away from home from time to time. Many in such a position would welcome your company when they, too, are on their own.

7. *What about chatlines?* Some people have developed meaningful, satisfying friendships in this way, rather like having

a pen friend. But there are drawbacks. First of all, there is no way of knowing how authentic your correspondent is being in his or her communication. Some people develop a total fantasy life over the Internet, so your relationship may be quite artificial. Then there is the question of safety; you don't want to put yourself in any danger. Internet chatlines are, in my opinion, a poor substitute for to face-to-face relationships.

8. *Buy a pet.* This, too, may be a substitute for other relationships, but if you are ready for the inconvenience and commitment involved in owning a pet, if your living accommodation is suitable, if the positives outweigh the negatives, and it is going to help you not to eat out of a sense of loneliness, then this could be the answer for you.

God's Word on Loneliness

When God created Adam He declared: 'It is not good that the man should be alone; I will make him a helper fit for him' (Genesis 2:18). In this context God is introducing the ordinance of marriage, but this is clearly not the lot for everyone. However, we do read in Psalm 68:6 that God 'settles the solitary in a home'. Through the imagery of the body of Christ we are called to recognise our mutual need of each other (1 Corinthians 12:12–27), and through that of God's building we are likened to bricks which are built together with the matrix of love (Ephesians 4:16). The Christian family has been designed to provide for the emotional needs of all who remain unattached but sometimes we fall painfully short in expressing the true heart of God.

However, in spite of our shortcomings, the family of God's people, the Church, is still the best environment for our social needs to be met.

There is no perfect church, and if there was then we would be well advised not to join, for then it would no longer be perfect! We, like everyone else, are all in the process of being made whole. As we grow in Christ and our spiritual and emotional needs are met, so we cease to be a part of the problem and become part of the answer. In spite of your own feelings of loneliness, you may have just what it takes to be God's answer to someone else.

Home Assignments

1. Do you identify with the activity void and the loneliness void? If so, what practical steps are you willing to take in order to stop yourself from turning to food?
2. Do you find yourself eating when watching the TV? Could this passive form of entertainment be partly responsible for your overeating? What are you prepared to do about it?
3. Make a list of things to do, which you can refer to whenever you feel bored. After practising this for a while, assess whether becoming purposefully involved in meaningful activity is helping to take your mind off food.
4. In what ways has food become for you a 'safe friend'?
5. Ask God to show you someone in your social circles who seems to be lonelier than you, someone who you might be a blessing to. Write down what you intend to do, and then do it!

7

The Spiritual Void

The human spirit has three elements: conscience, intuition and communion. It is through the conscience that we are able to discern between right and wrong, through intuition we may sense truth, even independently from our minds, and through communion we are able to reach out and worship God.

God's purpose in creating us was for fellowship. We were never meant to live out our existence apart from Him but, through the warmth of personal relationship, His intention is for each one of us to know Him intimately. Anything less than this leaves us frustrated and disappointed with life. We chase after shadows, thinking that they are the real thing, but they either elude us or fail to come up to expectations. Work, material things, thrills, religion – all these do not satisfy. Food does not satisfy, and even when we humans are fortunate to have it all – an adoring spouse, happy and loving children, selfless parents, loyal friends – we would still have to admit, if we are perfectly honest, a sense of something lacking.

St Augustine expressed this well when he wrote: 'O God,

Thou hast made us for Thyself and our hearts are restless until they find their rest in Thee.'[1] We have been created by God, for God and in the image of God, so not surprisingly there is, at the very core of our nature, a God-shaped hole, which nothing other than God Himself will ever be able to fill. We can sublimate our spiritual hunger, try to ignore it, call it by another name, but we cannot escape it.

Although we are all God's children by creation, known to Him so intimately that He is aware of our every thought and desire, we are unable by our own initiative to enjoy either the warmth or the benefits of such a relationship. This is because by nature we have inherited a congenital disease. It isn't a physical sickness, but a spiritual malaise which the Bible calls *sin*. It was universally handed down to us through the disobedience of our first parents, and has affected us all. Its main symptoms are a tendency to rebel against God's laws, an inordinate preoccupation with self and an inability to make any authentic spiritual connection with our Creator. This leaves us separated, lonely and frustrated. We may have some vague spiritual awareness, a deep-seated consciousness that there must be something more, for God has set eternity in our hearts (Ecclesiastes 3:11), but unless the fundamental hindrance of sin is first removed, all our strivings to find true spiritual fulfilment are destined to failure.

But God hasn't left us as orphans. He longs to draw us back into intimacy, to reconnect us with our Source and He has paved the way for this to be possible. More than 2,000 years ago God sent His only begotten Son into this fallen

---

[1] Augustine, *Confessions* (Oxford University Press USA, 1998)

world to take on our humanity, experience our pain and ultimately to give up His very life as a sacrifice for our sin. When, through the sacrificial death of Christ on the cross, the penalty for our sin was paid in full, God's holiness was satisfied and His mercy secured. By repentance and faith in what Jesus did for us that day – taking upon Himself, in His broken body, the combined sin of the whole of humanity – we may receive the grace of God's forgiveness for every wrong we have ever done, whether in thought, word or deed. Once healed of our spiritual disease, intimate fellowship with God is restored. Our spirits are made alive, our hearts find what they have been looking for all along and there is no longer any need to turn to food or any other inferior substitute to try and fill the gap.

(If you would like, at this point, further information as to how you can enter into a personal relationship with God through Jesus Christ, please turn to page 150 at the end of Chapter 10 where, under the heading 'Finding Peace with God and Peace with Yourself', you can read a step-by-step guide to help you do this.)

The Believer's Inner Hunger

But what if you already are a committed Christian? You have received Christ as your personal Saviour and Lord; you understand what is meant concerning this God-shaped hole and have already looked to God to fill it – and yet you are still overweight and still find yourself grazing on food. Do you still have an unfulfilled spiritual need?

Inner hunger may or may not be the dominant root of your disordered eating; it will vary from believer to believer.

I had been an overweight (at times obese) Christian for many, many years. I was in full-time Christian ministry and finding great fulfilment serving the Lord, and I was fortunate enough to have the emotional and practical support of a caring family and church. For me (it turned out) the predominant root to my own long-term eating problems was in my thought-life – mainly to do with false and unhelpful beliefs – but there were some spiritual elements as well. I noticed that when my own spiritual life was arid, I did have a tendency to eat more, or if I was so busy that I forgot my priorities and spent less time just being still before God, this too could affect my eating. Since the other functions of our spirit – the conscience and intuition – are both deadened to a degree when our intimacy with God is weak, I also found that when I was more distant from the Lord I was less able to receive guidance and therefore more prone to anxiety. Also, it goes without saying, that when our conscience isn't sharp we are more apt to fall into the sins of gluttony and lust, be it for food or any other object of our inordinate affection.

How Inner Hunger is Satisfied

It is through relationship, most intimately expressed as worship, that God has chosen to meet our spiritual hunger and to satisfy our hearts. You would think, then, that committed, born-again Christians would have no need in this area, but I meet many sincere Christians who deep down are still dissatisfied and who, if they are totally honest, would admit to still having a spiritual void in their lives. Oh, they may have an assurance of salvation; they may have peace with God inasmuch as they are secure in His love and acceptance; they read their Bibles, pray and go to church and they are involved in all manner of Christian activity. They know that they are better off than before they trusted in Christ, yet they remain to some extent disappointed and unfulfilled.

Perhaps you, too, feel this way. You *have* tasted the goodness of God and drunk from the river of His delights, and there was a time (maybe when you first surrendered your heart to Him) when you felt intoxicated with the new wine of 'first love' and were transported into heaven itself. But now such high points in your spiritual experience are just a memory and you have settled for the lowlands of mediocrity instead.

And yet you can't settle, because deep inside of you there is a strong spiritual urge which cannot be ignored. You may have tried to keep it suppressed with food and other things, but the hunger pangs will not go away. It isn't sufficient just to have correct doctrine, a kind of sterile orthodoxy which says all the right things but is devoid of life; there needs to be a thriving, vibrant, relationship, a divine interchange of love between the Spirit of God and the spirit of man, for this inner need to be met.

For some people this void is temporarily filled with all manner of subjective experiences: it may mean seeking out a prophet who will speak words of future greatness into your life, experiencing physical manifestations of various sorts, or it may be the intensity of emotionally charged music, but if you rely on them to fill your void they will eventually leave you feeling empty and looking around for the next 'shot'. And it isn't that these things are necessarily wrong or false. God does at times impact His people in a physical way, and He may indeed speak a prophetic word into our lives, but it is when these things become the *focus* of our experience that we are destined to be disappointed yet again.

In 2 Corinthians 11:3 Paul speaks of having '. . . a sincere and pure devotion to Christ.' What was he saying? I believe that what Paul wanted the Corinthians to understand was quite simply this – that Jesus is enough. Let me say that again a bit louder: JESUS IS ENOUGH! It is the Lord Himself, and not any of His blessings that can satisfy our deepest longings. We have been created for relationship and anything less than this falls far short of the mark. Madame Guyon wrote: 'Your spirit is so noble and so great that the most exalted gifts God has to give you cannot bring happiness to the spirit. . . not unless the Giver also gives himself.'[2] The psalmist echoes this sentiment through these words: 'As a deer pants for flowing streams, so pants my soul for you, O God!' (Psalm 42:1). What our spirits are crying out for is real and satisfying intimacy with God. And the good news is that it is within the reach of every one of us.

While visiting Jamaica a few years ago, I was struck by a message on a billboard advertising a brand of mineral water. The caption read: *Image is nothing, thirst is everything. OBEY YOUR THIRST!* Each one of us has a spiritual thirst for the things of God, whether we like to admit it or not. But we don't always listen to it (like we don't listen to our body to know our physical needs) for its cries are easily drowned out by the demands of our flesh nature.

---

[2] Guyon (Madame), *Experiencing the Depths of Jesus Christ* (Christian Books Publishing House, third edition, 1981)

Spiritual hunger and thirst are often addressed in the Bible through metaphors of food and drink. For instance, God promised His people that if they had listened to Him and walked in His ways, He would have 'fed them also with the finest of wheat' and satisfied them 'with honey from the rock' (Psalm 81:16, NKJV). Jesus said, when He addressed the crowds on the last day of the feast, 'If anyone thirsts, let him come to me and drink . . . Out of his heart will flow rivers of living water' (John 7:37–38). Again, when speaking with the Samaritan woman at the well, He said, 'If you knew the gift of God and who it is that is saying to you, "Give me a drink," you would have asked him, and he would have given you living water' (John 4:10). And through the prophet, Isaiah, He cries out to all of us:

> Ho! Everyone who thirsts, come to the waters: and you who have no money, come buy and eat. Yes, come, buy wine and milk, without money and without price. Why do you spend money for what is not bread, and your wages for what does not satisfy? Listen carefully to me and eat what is good, and let your soul delight itself in abundance. (Isaiah 55:1–2, NKJV)

You will find, in the stillness, when you dare to strip yourself of every prop and every distraction, that the voice of your spiritual thirst can be heard deep down inside you. If you obey that thirst, refusing to accept any placebo that may be offered to you instead, then it will lead you to the very throne room of God.

Each one of us is unique. None of us will find or experience God in exactly the same way. Abraham found Him under a starry sky, Moses in a burning bush, Jacob in a wrestling match, David on the Galilean hillside, Elijah in a still, small voice, Ezekiel in a vision of wheels within wheels. God deals with us as individuals. But His desire for each one of us is that we should experience His compassionate closeness; that we should know the fulfilment that comes from knowing Him intimately. He does not mean for such self-disclosure to be a one-off, introductory taste just to whet our appetites and tide us over until we get to heaven. Human relationships cannot survive on that level and neither can the ultimate relationship we were created for. He invites us to touch and taste and see and handle spiritual realities. He is waiting to reveal Himself to us in all of His ravishing fullness. If we seek Him and Him alone, then we shall surely find Him.

There are times, however, even in the lives of the most ardent God-seekers, when the Father seems to hide His face. It was from such a spiritual desert that the psalmist David wrote:

> I spread out my hands to you; my soul thirsts for you like a parched land.
> Answer me quickly, O Lord; my spirit fails! Hide not your face from me. (Psalm 143:6–7)

Such times can be quite perplexing and we might easily assume that there must be some heinous sin in our lives for God to withdraw in this way. Should this in fact be the case, then the Holy Spirit will certainly reveal it, but this may not be the cause at all. One reason why God permits such times in our lives is so that we will learn to love Him for Himself and not for His blessings – not even the blessing of His presence. But remember, when the sun goes behind a cloud it is no less near than when its rays are felt.

If you who have a weakness for food to fill your inner hungers, you will need to be especially careful at such times and to learn to let your hunger work for you and not against you. 'A worker's appetite works for him, for his hunger urges him on' (Proverbs 16:26, NASB). Difficult though these times are, they can be times of tremendous spiritual growth. Hang in there!

Hindrances to Fellowship

The devil comes to 'steal and kill and destroy' (John 10:10), and nowhere is this more evident than in his attempts to distract us from the pure worship of God. The devil craves worship for himself, which is why he rebelled against the Most High in the first place, and he will do anything he can to keep you and me from worshipping God now.

His most common ruse is to keep you so busy that you just don't find time for communion with God, or he tells you that you are wasting your time, or he distracts you through wandering thoughts or by having the phone ring. If you sense that you are neglecting your personal times of fellowship with the Lord, he burdens you down with guilt and condemnation so that you bar yourself from the fellowship you so desperately need, reasoning that you don't deserve it. Or if you do pray, he keeps you bogged down in methods, formulas and lists so that what should be a time of fulfilling fellowship becomes a matter of performance and dead works. The result? You start to find prayer boring! Or perhaps you're the practical sort, not really given to contemplation. You reason that this sort of thing is okay for some heavenly-minded mystics, but not for you.

Supposing that you do enter into a place of intimacy with God and begin to discover the delightfulness of His presence, what then? The devil now has a new approach: he whispers in your ear that it is all self-gratifying and therefore fleshly. 'Christianity should be about discipline and denying yourself,' he suggests. 'If you're enjoying it, it can't be good for you!' And so what happens? You back off, condemned and fearful of going any deeper.

God's Thirst

But God also has a thirst. He yearns for intimate fellowship with you and wants more than anything to draw close so that 'deep calls unto deep'. Jesus told the woman at the well: '. . . the hour is coming, and is now here, when the true worshippers will worship the Father in spirit and truth, for the Father *is seeking such people* to worship Him' (John 4:23 – italics mine). It is God who takes the initiative in seeking us out. In Psalm 27:8 we read: 'You have said, "Seek my face." My heart says to you, "Your face, Lord, do I seek."' Your hunger is a sure indication that God is doing the drawing.

Back at the dawn of creation God walked with Adam and Eve in the cool of the day, but then, through disobedience, that privilege of communion was forfeited. Only when Jesus came was the possibility of intimacy fully restored. As He walked among men He showed us the Father heart of God and beckoned us back to where we belong. Through Him we learn that God is loving, patient and forgiving and that He wants us to be reconciled to Himself. Although the Heavenly Father is holy and dwells in unapproachable light, yet we can now draw near through the merits of His Son and call Him by the familiar name of 'Abba, Father'. The blood of Jesus, the spotless Lamb of God was shed, the sacrificial price for sin was paid in full and a new and living way has been opened up to us whereby we can come with boldness into the very presence of Almighty God, and worship before His throne.

With reverence and humility He invites us to draw close. The veil of the Temple, symbolically rent from top to bottom as Jesus gave up His life for us on the cross, no longer separates us from our Source. We come into the Holy of Holies and, as the cloud of His presence envelops us, we behold in the Spirit, the very face of our Beloved, and our hungry souls, at last, are satisfied.

Are you eating to try and fill a spiritual void within you? If what I have written thus far in this section has served to stir you up and whet your appetite then I am glad. You are discovering yet another area of self-awareness which will allow you to live authentically without needing to look to food and other things to satisfy. The Lord has said: 'You will seek me and find me when you seek me with all your heart' (Jeremiah 29:13), and this is most certainly true. When we come before God's throne to worship, God is not reading our lips, He is reading our hearts.

A Spiritual Journey

Some of you, recognising your inner thirst, may be asking the question, 'How can I find this intimacy?' I am reluctant to prescribe 'methods' of seeking God, for what helps one person probably won't help another, but there is a biblical

model I would like to share briefly with you – one that I
have personally found very useful in helping me to 'draw
near'. It describes worship as a spiritual journey, and is
based upon the construction of the Tabernacle we read
about in the book of Exodus. Our journey takes us from the
'outer court' of praise and thanksgiving, through the Holy
Place and on into the Holy of Holies.

We are exhorted in Psalm 100:4 to 'enter His gates with
thanksgiving and His courts with praise!' This is the start of
our journey, and for the Jewish believer it was as far as he
could go unless he was a priest. Sadly many believers today,
unaware of their priestly privileges, restrict themselves to
the outer court and worship afar off. In the outer court we
may ask ourselves how, or in what ways, God is relating to
us within the realm of our own personal, present experience. What has He done for each one of us that we can
thank and praise Him for? This may include the 'ever-
greens' of appreciating the fact that we are 'ransomed,
healed, restored, forgiven', or that God is providing for all
my needs, guiding me, protecting me, sustaining me, com-
forting me, teaching me and helping me. There may be
something current and specific which fills my thoughts and
calls forth my praise but even if I am going through a rough
time, and there seems to be little to thank Him for in my
own life, I can always praise Him for all that He is in His
own right, irrespective of how I feel. Even if tears are cours-
ing down my cheeks because of the pain of a present situation, I can still set my will to praise Him, for He is worthy. 'I
will bless the Lord at all times; His praise shall *continually* be
in my mouth' (Psalm 34:1).

You may find it helpful to sing your praise back to Him by

way of simple made-up songs or by providing your own melodies to appropriate Bible verses. If you want to shout, sing, cry out, sigh or laugh, that's all right; you can stand, sit, kneel, raise or clap your hands, even dance, if it expresses the true sentiments of your heart. While at this stage in the journey we are focusing our thanksgiving towards God as the object of our praise, it is we ourselves who remain very much the subject. This is *my* experience I am singing about; I am expressing the realities of how God relates to *me*.

If we wish to travel further we must begin now to lose sight of our own experience and focus more on the character and person of the One who is the object of our worship. Matt Redman observes: 'There's definitely a different dynamic in worship that kicks in when we fix our eyes firmly on Jesus.'[3] Worship is all about ascribing worth, and God's worth is not only in what He does – this is secondary – but intrinsically in who He is. Now we begin to speak and sing of His loving kindness and faithfulness, of His mercy and truth, of His beauty and splendour and of His incomparable love. As our mouths show forth His praise, so our hearts aspire to reach up to Him and to know Him for who He is. 'Draw me closer,' is our cry. We express our hunger, identifying closely with the psalmist who exclaimed: 'Whom have I in Heaven but You; and there is none upon the earth I desire besides You' (Psalm 73:25, NKJV).

We are now in the Holy Place, but there is yet a deeper place we may journey to if we truly press into worship. Aspiration is good for it will urge us forward, but God's

---

[3] Redman, Matt, *The Unquenchable Worshipper* (Kingsway, 2001)

promise is that He will satisfy our thirst and fill the hungry with good things. I see the Holy of Holies as a place of response to the awareness we have received in the Holy Place. For instance, I may have been focusing my thoughts on the greatness of God and the fact that He is the Lord of the whole earth. Now I should respond appropriately to that revelation. What is a suitable response? Firstly my heart will want to express that lordship in a personal way, and then, because He is my Lord, I will come and bow down at His throne. His name is higher than any other name so I bow my knee in humble acknowledgement of this fact and bring my whole being to Him in full and glad surrender, asking Him to reign in me. If there are issues over which I have been struggling (maybe some areas of our relationship with food) now is a good time to yield, so I come and lay everything down at His feet.

Supposing that in the Holy Place we have dwelt upon the holiness of God; what is the worshipful response to that going to be? Perhaps we will sense our own sinfulness and unworthiness. We know that we are cleansed (for we couldn't come this far without such assurance), but now our hearts just long to be pure even as He is pure. Or if we have become conscious of the giving heart of Jesus, of the sacrifice He paid on the cross, then we may experience a reciprocal desire to give ourselves back to Him as fully as possible. Inasmuch as we are able, we lay down our own life too, that out of love for Him we may be willing to give up anything and everything. The challenge of voluntarily giving up an excessive amount of high-calorie, low-nutri- ent food seems, in this context, to be superfluous; it is the least we can do.

Even as we give all to Jesus, so He gives Himself to us. This is hard to put into words, but in these moments of deep, intimate worship, there is an exchange of love which transcends all explanation, and even if it might be explained, to do so would merely cheapen it. The early saints sometimes called this the 'gaze of the soul'. It embodies a time when the eyes of our spiritual understanding are enlightened, not so much in a way that makes sense to the mind, but in a way which deeply satisfies the soul and fills the most profound longings of our hearts. When we find this place of intimacy, let us not try to fill the silence with superfluous activity, nor yet to leave the place too quickly. Rather let us be like Mary who sat at Jesus' feet in loving, adoring worship, attentive only to His voice, desiring only to do His will.

At the end of the day intimate worship is all about the response of our hearts to the Person who God is. As the Living God Himself fills our vision and becomes the focus of all our thoughts and desires, we will not only *bring* a sacrifice, we will become the sacrifice. The worth-ship of Jesus is not demonstrated in high-sounding words and sentimental melodies, but in the reality of a surrendered life. This, too, forms the basis of having a Spirit-controlled appetite, for when, having been liberated from the yoke of bondage to diets and taken control of our lives, we lovingly and submissively relinquish that control to the will of God, we find that food itself has to surrender its throne. God begins to reign in our lives without a rival. The spiritual void in our spirits is filled; at last we are truly satisfied.

Home Assignments

1. Seek to become more aware of your inner hunger. Whenever you feel it, get alone with God and spend time in worship. You may like to use worship CDs to help you.

2. Spend time daily seeking God for Himself. Push through the distractions and refuse to settle for second best.

3. If you have never experienced this intimate relationship with God, it could be that the barrier of sin in your life has never been effectively dealt with. Turn to page 150 at the end of Chapter 10 to the section entitled 'Finding Peace with God and Peace with Yourself' for further instruction.

4. Having now learned about many aspects of emotional eating you can start to complete the Emotional Eating Log which is found in Appendix 2. Keep adding to it as you become aware of new dynamics in your life.

8

Fearful of Being Slim

We are all familiar with the fear of being fat which is behind so much of the thinking of people with eating disorders such as anorexia nervosa or bulimia, but a person's eating behaviour can just as equally be governed by a fear of being slim. At first suggestion this may appear ludicrous and, you might wonder, if someone was to have such a fear, why would they even bother to read this book? But I put it to you that while, on the one hand, you may long with all your heart to lose weight and be slim, you may, on the other hand, have a subconscious pull in the opposite direction – that is, to remain fat.

Maybe your track record of dieting is one in which you have experienced a measure of success, but then, inexplicably, at a certain point, everything appears to go haywire and you find yourself sabotaging your own efforts. It doesn't make sense; yet looking back you see that this has been your pattern time and time again. One possible reason for this is that deep down you are fearful of becoming slim. As we seek now to explore this phenomenon, ask the Holy

Spirit to show you which factors, if any, apply to you. Remember: knowing the truth is our first step in being set free.

Fear of the Unknown

Perhaps you have never known what it is like to be slim. Maybe throughout your entire adult life a major part of your identity has been that you are big and fat. You may not like the image, but at least it is familiar. A new body, you feel, will give you a brand new image and deep down this is scary. How will people relate to you? If you have had fat friends, will they still wish to associate with you when you are different to them, when you have succeeded where they have failed? Perhaps they will even be jealous of your new look and start to backbite and find fault. What if they reject you? This can be very scary. You may also wonder whether, having become slim, you would be able to maintain it – after all, your track record has been one of measured success followed by dismal failure. Why put your neck on the line again?

If your size and eating problem have been the focus of your own or other people's attention, what will take its place when the problem ceases to exist? How will you fill this void? At least when you are fat, and going from one diet or slimming club to another, you have something to talk about. Others are interested to know how you are doing, they rally round to encourage you in your latest endeavour. But once you become slim and everyone has got used to seeing you that way, there will come a time when your slimness will be taken for granted. If being fat has fulfilled your need for attention, then it may subconsciously work against your resolve to succeed. On the other hand, if your personal need is for anonymity rather than attention, you may feel that were you to become slim you would be noticed more.

Fear of Vulnerability

The presence we project onto the world is, to some extent, related to our physical size. I remember when I was still at school the phenomenal power the deputy head held over us pupils. She must have weighed in easily at 20 stone, and while she was generally disliked and we made fun of her behind her back, we held the greatest respect for her awesome presence! It wasn't just her size, I suppose it must also have been the stern expression and the booming voice, but the overall effect was to intimidate us into unquestioned subjection. She never had any discipline problems to contend with, work was always handed in on time, and even parents fought shy of taking her on. Had she been slim, would her role as disciplinarian have been quite as easy, I wonder?

As a child, Terry had always been thin. His personality was quite passive and he wasn't particularly good at sports either, so he earned the reputation of being 'thin and weedy' and was often the subject of taunts and jeers. He eventually took solace in food and his 'weediness' disappeared. Then as a middle-aged adult, years of overindulgence and a liking for high-calorie fatty food had resulted in a dangerously large abdomen. He knew that he needed to lose weight, but at the back of his mind was the association of being skinny with verbal abuse. To him, weight loss represented vulnerability.

Tanya, on the other hand, had always been tubby, even as a child, but she was also quite tall. There had been times when she, too, had been picked on for her size, but she had learnt that attack was the best form of defence and very soon no one took her on because they knew that they would probably come off worst. She even became a guardian figure to others who felt safe under the shadow of her size. What could have worked against her was actually working for her, making her a force to be reckoned with and intimidating her opponents. She wanted to become slim but feared the vulnerability of not having the extra weight to throw around any more.

What we observe in each of these examples is how excess weight may be used to compensate for inner insecurity. When you are big and take up more space, people seem to respect you more. I mean, who would consider hiring a puny looking individual as a bouncer at a nightclub? Are there any physical advantages that you feel you have now, which you would lose were you to become slim?

Fear of Intimacy

Most of us relate being slim with being more sexually attractive. While this is a sought-after goal for some people, for others it is fraught with fears. If sex is something you wish to avoid, then it may seem advantageous to you to remain fat.

Andrea was postmenopausal and frankly no longer had the slightest interest in sex. Her husband had accepted the situation, but Andrea felt that if she lost weight he would have a renewed interest in her body. She didn't want to send out any signals that would encourage this kind of attention so, much as a part of her wanted to be slim again, she resisted change for fear of the demands that might be made upon her.

Courtney, on the other hand, was unmarried and, because of issues in her past, had always steered clear of any relationship which she thought could eventually lead to physical intimacy. To her, sex seemed dirty and shameful and so to minimise the possibility of being a sexual object to any man, she preferred to remain inside the prison of her fat body, which was (by her own reckoning) less desirable. And what was the reason for this? She had been raped by her uncle when she was just a young girl.

Behind a fear of sex there often lies a fear of intimacy and this can exist even in the most committed Christian marriage. It isn't just the physical intimacy which is a problem, but the feeling of being exposed and emotionally vulnerable which it also involves. I once heard the word 'intimacy' broken up as 'into-me-see' which I think is quite a profound link of ideas. If you are insecure about your own self-worth you may fear nakedness as it removes the mask, allowing your partner to 'see into you' as you really are. In the Garden of Eden we read that Adam and Eve were to begin with naked and unashamed, but once they had sinned they became self-conscious in a negative way and hid from God's presence. Eventually they covered their nakedness with fig leaves. Perhaps you, too, carry a deep-seated shame about who you really are. Much as you may fantasise about being slim and sexy, you don't want to face the reality of a committed relationship either emotionally or physically.

Fear of intimacy, born out of negative past relationships, may prevent you from forming new relationships. When a person has been badly hurt it is natural to wish to avoid the same thing happening again and one way to achieve this is by an appearance which gives a signal saying: 'Don't come near me.' Of course, there are men who, contrary to what the media messages portray, are more attracted to larger women, and vice versa, but if you are obese and someone shows interest in you, you may reason, in a self-deprecating way, that he or she can't amount to much or they would be looking elsewhere!

Lack of trust in yourself or your spouse could also discourage weight loss. Maybe you are dissatisfied in your relationship and fantasise about finding greater happiness with someone else so you may decide to play safe and appear less desirable. The Lord showed a married woman who attended a Fit For Life Forever seminar that her fear of being slim was linked with a past misdemeanour through which she had become pregnant by another man and had an abortion. She had since found reconciliation with both her spouse and God but had been unable to really forgive or trust herself. Not only did she not trust herself to being attractive again, but felt that she no longer deserved it. The truth was revealed for what it was and through prayer she was set free.

Maybe it isn't yourself who you can't trust, but your spouse. If you are afraid that your overweight spouse may look elsewhere should he lose his flab, then you might seek to sabotage his or her efforts to get trim. A wife might pile extra helpings on her husband's plate, or a distrustful husband might keep assuring his wife that she looks just fine as she is – why bother to lose weight at all? (Now don't go suspecting your husband or wife of not trusting you just because they happen to convey acceptance of your size – they probably genuinely want to lift the pressure off you.)

Fear of Being Valued for the Wrong Reasons

One of our primary needs is, I believe, to be valued. Some people may wish that they had some special ability whereby others would need them, while others, possessing such attributes, remain insecure as to whether others would still want them if they were not so spectacularly gifted. The same rationale can apply to size. If it makes a person more desirable to be slim, is this a valid foundation for a relationship, be it intimate or professional in nature?

There is some statistical evidence that, all other things being equal, slim people have a greater chance of getting a job promotion. You want to get ahead, but the thought of acquiescing to this kind of prejudicial stereotyping is obnoxious to you. You determine to prove the statistics wrong and make your personal protest against such thinking. You will make it, in spite of your size! Well, if this is you, I do admire your pluck, but you are paying a heavy price (literally!) Do make sure that you are not cutting off your nose to spite your face. Within a marriage we can play the same sort of games. You could use your obesity to test your spouse's commitment by remaining fat and conveying the message: 'Love me, love my fat!'

Fear of Cancer

A man attending a Fit For Life Forever seminar told me how his mother had died of cancer when he was still a child and that many other members of his family had succumbed to the same disease. This had produced in him a fear of contracting the same, often-deadly illness. Since one of the symptoms of cancer is weight loss this man reasoned that as long as he wasn't losing weight he didn't have cancer. Although he knew that he was overweight and therefore in danger of other obesity-related illness, his fear reinforced his spurious logic.

The Common Denominators to Our Fears

We have looked briefly at a number of fears which may consciously or otherwise sabotage our efforts to lose weight: fear of the unknown, fear of vulnerability, fear of intimacy and sex, fear of having false value and fear of cancer. But the root of many of these fears is very often unresolved past hurts and low self-esteem; issues which are the subject of the following two chapters. To overcome, you will need to develop four areas of your life. These are: becoming more secure as a person, the willingness to take risks, the development of trust, and allowing yourself to be more vulnerable.

As you continue in this study, the same God who is already setting you free from your diet mentality and obsession with food is at work on the inside to free you from all your anxiety and fears. Fears are usually based on a lie, so if we deal with the lies then the fear will die. God's Word not only offers us truth, but also hope. Norman Wright says: 'The antidote for fear is hope. Hope is a powerful positive drive. . . It is like a magnet that draws you towards your goal. . . God's message of hope to us is "You can do it. Trust in Me and allow Me to free you from your prison of fears."'[1] God's Word promises us that, '. . . He who began a good work in you will bring it to completion. . . ' (Philippians 1:6). Remember, He is changing you from the inside out, so don't worry if the weight isn't budging as quickly as you hoped; God is laying a firm foundation in your life. As your thoughts are renewed and your emotions healed, as you grow in trust and dependency upon God's grace, your life is being radically and permanently changed. You may still see yourself as fat on the outside, but on the inside you are already much, much thinner. Hang in there!

Home Assignments

1. Are you in any way afraid of being slim? If so, why is this?
2. Start to pray about possible root causes to your fear so that as you learn more you will receive revelation you can act on.

---

[1] Wright, H. Norman, *How To Get Along With Almost Anyone* (Word Publishing, 1989)

9

Facing the Past

A s you have read through the last three chapters of this book you will have become increasingly aware of the enormous role that our emotions play in the way in which we relate to food. So far I have addressed emotions which lie mainly at the conscious level of our being: fear, anxiety, boredom and loneliness are feelings which, generally speaking, are easy for us to be in touch with. You are learning to identify ways in which you, personally, have been using food to stop or prevent you from feeling emotions which are painful and uncomfortable, and hopefully you are discovering some practical and spiritual ways in which you can bring some measure of control into your life.

It may be, however, that as you grow in your self-awareness and begin to address the relevant issues which I have raised so far, you will begin to feel increasingly uncomfortable, nervous, irritable and fearful. Having begun to face these issues, your anxiety, instead of diminishing, is growing? What could be the cause of this unrest?

What may well be happening inside you is that God is gradually removing the protective layers in order to get to the root issues in your life. We have begun with the known and conscious elements of our being: our dislike of our body size and desire to lose weight and our present thoughts and emotions connected with our relationship with food and dieting. Then we have delved a bit deeper and begun to see that many of our eating problems actually have very little to do with food! Now it is time, with God's help, for us to face the hurt child within us.

We all have a past. Some of it was good but, for most of us, there were bad bits as well. We live in a fallen world and one of the consequences of that is that we have, at times, been on the receiving end of other people's fallen natures and have suffered deep emotional pain as a result. While the hurts we have incurred will certainly not have been limited to childhood, it is the pain associated with this period of our lives which carries the greatest consequences. For one thing, they lie deeply buried. Also, as children, we were at our most vulnerable and lacked the maturity to cope with experiences which we did not understand. If you have been using food to shield yourself from your past, then you may be finding – as this protective façade is systematically being removed – that you are becoming more and more agitated.

Please understand that this is normal and that it is really a good sign because it indicates your submission to the Holy Spirit and a willingness to allow God to deal with the root issues. Do not be fearful. Not even a sparrow can fall to the ground without the knowledge of your Heavenly Father. He knew you from your mother's womb and is acquainted with all your ways (Psalm 139:3 and 13). Jesus, having come in the flesh, has personally experienced all the grief and sorrows which are common to man. He has known suffering beyond what any of us have ever had to experience. He was betrayed and forsaken, despised and rejected. He was used, abused and falsely accused, not once or twice, but constantly. He endured torture – mentally, emotionally and physically – and finally He was delivered up to an agonising death for a crime He didn't commit. He has indeed stood in your shoes – understand and take comfort from this. And now He is here to help you, not by slapping a plaster on your wounds, but by performing the necessary surgery that will take the sting out of all your past hurts and make you whole again.

Ghosts From Our Past

What kinds of painful childhood experiences are we talking about here? It doesn't have to be something at the top of the Richter scale like losing your parents in a fatal accident or having your house burn to the ground. It could include such things as the death of someone close, a divorce or any experience which gave you a sense of abandonment. Or maybe you were deeply unsettled by a house move or a change of school or were shamed by the behaviour of a family member. Maybe you endured derision and criticism from either a parent or sibling, or were bullied at school. Abuse, be it verbal, emotional or physical always leaves its scars. As a child you may have accepted such treatment as normal, only realising as you got older how dysfunctional your family situation really was.

Or the pain may be derived from events far more subtle than those given above. It may have simply been that your parents were very busy and so you didn't receive the emotional support you needed, or that they tried to live out their own ambitions through you, seeking to enforce their own plans and wishes on your life without taking due account of your own desires and feelings. Perhaps you were required to shoulder burdens too heavy for your age and maturity, like having to take care of a younger sibling or being a parent's primary source of emotional support. You may have been asked to adjudicate in quarrels between your parents or had one parent confide in you about the perceived inadequacies of the other.

What if your father or mother was a rigid disciplinarian who exercised excessive control, or a perfectionist who was difficult to please and punished shortcomings severely? What if the atmosphere in the home was often tense, with outbursts of anger, or if tensions were felt but never acknowledged openly? You could easily feel deep down that you were intrinsically flawed or that you were to blame for any unhappiness. If your mother was herself obsessive about her weight, then you may have become overly self-conscious about your own shape and size also, especially if attention was constantly being drawn in a negative way as to how you were beginning to put on weight.

Hurts from childhood are as much about perceptions as they are facts. Sometimes we simply failed to understand the dynamics of what was going on around us and put a more negative spin on events than was really the case. So it wasn't that Daddy didn't love you; he simply found it difficult to demonstrate his affection. Mum didn't really abandon you, but her own mother was becoming frail and demanded more of her time and attention. To know is to understand, but you were too young to know and you didn't understand – you just felt hurt.

How does a child handle such things? How did you? Lacking understanding, unable to communicate what you were experiencing, having no frame of reference and feeling frightened, vulnerable, insecure, angry, ashamed, let down or inadequate – how did you survive? Some children would have become disruptive at school or run away, or buried themselves in the fantasy life of books, but you took another course of action – you turned to food.

By self-medicating on foods which are enjoyable to our palates, or which we associate with pleasure, we can gain temporary relief from our distress (in the same way as addicts do with drugs) while even the discomfort we associate with overeating can distract us from the deeper discomfort of our emotional state. Where there is unresolved pain from childhood you may still be eating today as your way of coping with these deep-seated issues.

One high-profile example of emotional eating is that of Oprah Winfrey, who has shared openly about her own use of food to help alleviate the pain of her lack of love and attention in infancy. Until she discovered and dealt with this root cause she continued to binge and yo-yo diet.

Past Pain – Present Response

It is possible that painful events in the past, which at that time caused you to turn to food, have, over the years, been healed, and yet the habitual response has not been broken. These habits may remain with you today, long after the emotional need has passed.

An example of this is Jenny, a lady in her mid-forties, who attended a Fit For Life Forever seminar. She told me how, since being a child, she had found it impossible to come into her home in the late afternoon without being compelled to raid the larder. She was fine at any other time of the day, but between the hours of 3pm and 5pm it was a real problem and she couldn't understand why. Then, as she prayed about it, the Lord took her back into her child-hood when, every evening after school, she would visit her grandmother and stay until her mother collected her from work. Her grandmother (as well as being a kindly soul) was a fantastic cook and would always have home-baked cakes and biscuits ready for her when she got in. These were such happy days for Jenny. But then her grandmother died and she became a 'latchkey kid' going home to an empty house after school. She missed her grandmother dreadfully and would console herself with food from her mother's kitchen. At this stage eating was not only a habitual response, it was also, in her grief and loneliness, fulfilling a deep emotional need. In time her wounds healed and life went on. As an adult she felt no pain associated with these past events, but the behaviour had persisted and, on a subconscious level, was causing her to look for food whenever she came home to an empty house at a similar hour to when she used to come in from school.

This kind of behaviour, because it affects our subcon-scious, can be hard to recognise. But if, as you seek to be analytical about your own eating, you recognise a pattern for which there seems to be no logical explanation, this may be the answer. As you open up to the Holy Spirit He will show you these deep-seated roots. Sometimes they will be associated with emotional pain and sometimes they won't. But don't worry, God is familiar with your whole life history and won't reveal things to you until you are equipped to handle them. As you familiarise yourself with this book you are being given the tools and insights to deal with such situations and it will become easier.

In Jenny's case, once the habit was seen for what it was, it was then a simple matter of praying a prayer of release and a very short time afterwards her behaviour changed. She knew that she didn't need those old props any more and within three weeks her old destructive eating habits were gone.

How Can I Tell if I Need Emotional Healing?

If you are identifying with what I am describing in this chapter, you probably are in need of emotional healing. Here are some more clues to help you assess the level of your own needs:

- There is a reaction within you when certain topics are brought up.
- You want to forget about the past because it brings back too much pain.
- You avoid anything that reminds you of a particular negative experience.
- You experience painful flashback memories and / or bad dreams.
- You overreact in situations which trigger a painful memory from the past.
- You are consciously depressed, angry and resentful.
- You cannot forgive people for the way they hurt you.

- You feel guilty and ashamed when you think about your past.
- Your present lifestyle or relationship situation mirrors the past in such a way as could lead to further hurt or abuse, e.g. having left one abusive relationship you have walked straight back into another.

If you identified with any of the above responses this could be a good indicator of your need to be healed. However, let me say from the outset, that I am not taking you on a witch hunt to unearth all the painful events of your past. Where there is a need for you to revisit your past and when the time is right, God will make it clear to you. First of all He will have been preparing you for this time of self-disclosure so that you are ready to face your pain. Then He will gently bring things to a head so that you can't run away from your pain any more. He will grant you the grace to be honest with yourself and give you the strength to do all that it necessary on your part to bring healing and release.

The reality of your situation is this: to release your excess weight you are first going to have to release food as an emotional prop in your life, and the key to your being able to do that is to find healing for your pain. Don't worry, help is at hand! When you have allowed God to touch your life in this deep and personal way, such beauty and radiance is going to emanate from you. There will be a new softness and peace in your demeanour and you will walk six inches taller! Are you ready for this? Then let me take you through the steps which will lead you there.

God is our Healer (Exodus 15:26) not just physically, but also emotionally. The word 'salvation', which we apply primarily to having received the forgiveness of our sins, applies, in the fullest sense, to being made whole. Isaiah, prophesying concerning the suffering of Christ on our behalf, tells us:

> Surely He has borne our griefs and carried our sorrows. Yet we esteemed Him stricken, smitten by God and afflicted. But He was wounded for our transgressions, He was bruised for our iniquities; the chastisement of our peace was upon Him and by His stripes we are healed. (Isaiah 53: 5–6, NKJV)

Jesus has felt your pain; He has carried your sorrows and He waits to set you free.

Four Steps to Freedom

Although you can go through these steps on your own, you might find it helpful to go through them with a mature Christian who you feel you can really trust. Pray together before you start to share, asking God to gently lead and guide you into all truth and to give you the grace to follow His instruction.

Step one: Face up to your hurtful past. It is absolutely vital that you turn and face your painful memory, but know that, in reality, it cannot physically hurt you any more. Try to be as honest as you can about the situation that has caused you so much distress. You shouldn't ignore or make light of it or try to pretend that it never happened. Even if you feel, as an adult, that it was just a matter of distorted reality and that you are probably making a mountain out of a molehill, it is your inner child that needs to face the pain. If you have experienced some injustice, then know that anger is a valid response to such treatment. It is not a sin to be angry, only to express your anger in such a way as injures others (which is what often happens when we try to bottle it up). We can be angry and still express it in a respectful way. We should never be controlled by our anger. 'Speak when you're angry, and you'll make the best speech you'll ever regret!'[1] So face up to and acknowledge your pain and injury, even the desire to take revenge, if it is there inside you. Give yourself permission to grieve and let out all the pain that you have hitherto suppressed with food. As you face the pain, don't be ashamed to weep or cry out; simply pour out your heart before God, holding nothing back.

Step two: Be proactive in dealing with your hurt. What this means is that you need to take responsibility for the pain you have been carrying over the years. 'Placing the blame elsewhere doesn't help, because then only that other. . . person can restore the balance. If you take responsibility, then you have the power to set things right.'[2] Other people were certainly responsible for the injustice, and your hurt response to that offence has been understandable, but you cannot blame *them* for the response *you* chose to make. We cannot, and we must not, allow other people's weaknesses to control us and to mess up our lives.

Even though historically you may correctly view yourself

---

[1] Peter, Lawrence J., from 'Anger Quotes', on Quotes of the Heart website: www.heartquotes.net/Anger.html (accessed 09/12/06)

[2] Lieberman, David J., *Make Peace With Anyone* (St Martin's Press, 2002)

as a victim, this is an unhealthy and self-defeating self-image when carried into the present. People with a victim mentality often feel powerless to change their lives and circumstances and blame others for their unhappy lot. They do not wish to take responsibility for their pain and justify holding onto resentment and unforgiveness. Not only will this view of life make you powerless, it will stop you from maturing emotionally and from being productive in your everyday life. It will ultimately lead to self-destruction. You don't have to let your past permeate your present and pollute your future!

When Jesus addressed the paralysed man who had been sitting by the pool of Bethesda for many years, waiting for his miracle, He asked him this question: 'Do you want to be healed?' (John 5:5–9). What a strange question that appears to be. Surely after hanging around for so long it should have been obvious that he wanted to be healed! But I need to ask you the same thing. Do *you* want to be made whole? Oh, I know you want to control your weight, or you wouldn't be reading this book, but that isn't the question. I'm delving much deeper than that! I'm frankly not interested in a superficial, cosmetic solution to your problem; I want to see you set free on the inside, so that your body will then just fall in line with your change in attitudes and perspectives.

There's hardly a person in Europe who hasn't heard of the Leaning Tower of Pisa in Italy which has been slowly tilting for over 800 years, and could, at some point, come crashing down. So what should they do? The secretary for tourism at Pisa has remarked: 'The problem is to halt the leaning, not to straighten the tower. If the tower were to be straightened out then there would be no more tourism and we would be ruined!'[3] So the parallel is this: do you want to be totally healed, or just to feel better? Do you want to be straightened up, or merely to have your leaning halted a bit?

Step three: Agree with God's word concerning forgiveness. It is Alexander Pope who is credited with the famous saying: 'to err is human; to forgive is divine.' The only valid scriptural way of dealing with emotional injury is through the act of forgiveness. In the Lord's Prayer, which most of us are familiar with, Jesus taught us to pray: '. . . forgive us our debts, as we also have forgiven our debtors' (Matthew 6:12). He further went on to say, '. . . if you forgive others their trespasses, your heavenly Father will also forgive you, but if you do not forgive others their trespasses, neither will your Father forgive your trespasses' (Matthew 6:14–15). The apostle Paul, writing to the church at Ephesus (Ephesians 4:32), also wrote: 'Be kind to one another, tender-hearted, forgiving one another, as God in Christ forgave you.'

Unforgiveness can be likened to 'a videotape in the mind playing its tormenting re-runs, shackling us to the unremitting pain of a raging memory. It leaves us locked in a straitjacket of our own resentment.'[4] Notice from this definition that the torment, the pain and the prison are all experienced by the one who chooses to hold onto the hurt. The perpetrator,

---

[3] Quoted in Tripp, Dick, 'Forgiveness: What it is and Why it Matters', and 'Exploring Faith Today' (New Zealand: Dick Tripp Publications)

[4] Seamands, Dr David, 'Forgiveness: The Power to Change the Past', on the Narramore Christian Foundation Psychology for Living website: www.ncfliving.org (accessed 28/11/06)

on the other hand, may not even be aware of the pain, and for him or her life may well go on as normal.

When a person exercises true forgiveness it takes full account of the offence committed. Forgiveness is neither to deny nor to seek to forget; it does not condone or excuse the fault of the other; it doesn't condemn and it doesn't seek justice or compensation. It looks the perpetrator square in the face, sees the injustice for what it is and then freely and spontaneously chooses to release and absolve the other in spite of all the suffering the offence has brought. A tall order? Certainly! But you know what? When we give and go on giving the gift of forgiveness, the payback for ourselves is that our pain eventually disappears and we are healed. When we release the offender, it is we, the offended, who are set free.

Step four: Just do it! Well, are you ready to take this step? It makes no difference whether the person (or persons) you need to forgive is alive or has long since died; it matters not whether the offence was small or great, a one-off incident or a lifetime of abuse. What God requires of you, in order to make you whole, is that you as an act of your will choose from your heart to let go of your resentment and simply forgive. It may help you to recognise that 'hurt people hurt people', and that the one who offended you probably acted out of the pain he or she was experiencing as a result of another's offence. And if you are perfectly honest wouldn't it also be true that, due to your own pain, you have at times overreacted in ways which have wounded others? Dare we be too judgemental of others when we stand in need of so much forgiveness ourselves?

Don't concern yourself too much about 'feeling' forgiveness – this will follow in due course. The important thing is to choose to do what is right. It is difficult, but God never asks anything of us without providing us with the necessary grace to fulfil His commands. You may feel that the one who hurt you doesn't deserve to be forgiven, but ought rather to be punished. Forgiveness doesn't negate the law. If a crime has been committed (for instance if you have been raped) then the one who has committed the offence should pay the price and reap what has been sown. But vengeance isn't your remit – that belongs to the justice system and ultimately to God. '"Vengeance is mine; I will repay," says the Lord' (Romans 12:19).

If you have been living in an abusive situation, forgiveness does not automatically imply that you must continue to live under such duress. Obviously God's best is reconciliation, but this needs both parties to be prepared to do whatever it takes to move forward and this, sadly, isn't always the case. We may forgive the lion for biting off one of our hands, but only a fool will then extend to it the other! You can walk out of an abusive environment yet still hold forgiveness in your heart for your abuser.

When you are ready, here is what I want you to do. Find a quiet place, free from distractions and make out a list of all the people who God brings to mind who have injured you in some way and who you know you need to forgive. Then, either on your own, or with a trusted friend, make this your prayer:

> Dear loving heavenly Father, I come to You, bringing all the burden of the hurt and pain I have carried over the years. (Here you can express, in your own words, your grief, pain,

anger and resentment honestly to God.) I know that the negative feelings I have held in my heart over these hurts have messed up my life and even affected the way I eat. I take responsibility for the pain I am carrying and choose to be made whole. I cannot do this on my own but I believe that even now Your Holy Spirit is here with me to help me to do this difficult thing. Therefore now, with His help, and because I know that it is the right thing to do, I choose, as a free act of my will, to forgive totally and without obligation . . . (Here name the person or persons who you need to forgive). I let go of the anger, resentment and unforgiveness. I let go of any wish or plan for revenge, and I let go of all the pain now, in Jesus' name. Amen.

Once you have prayed it is helpful to pray blessing upon the one you have just forgiven as it will help seal the release you have exercised. But you should do this also every time a memory of that person floods back into your mind. The devil isn't going to give up without a struggle and will probably try to make you dwell again on your painful memories if you let him. By immediately turning your negative thoughts into a positive act of blessing you quench Satan's fiery darts and they cannot harm you.

God loves you so much, but He also loves those who have hurt you and wants them to be healed just as much as He desires this for you. As you continually lift these ones to the Lord in prayer He will begin to reveal to you His own heart of love for them and may even show you practical ways in which you can demonstrate that love towards them, so becoming an answer to your own prayers. Is this asking too much? In your own strength, it may well be impossible, but God's grace is perfected in your weakness. Dare to trust Him in this and it will not only hasten your own healing but open up the windows of heaven and lift you to God.

Home Assignments

1. Do you find yourself eating in specific places or at specific times without knowing the reason why? Could it be linked to a painful experience from your past, even though you no longer feel the pain?

2. When God shows you the connection, pray along these lines: 'Dear God, thank you that you have already healed me of the pain of this memory which I believe is linked with my present disordered eating. I now claim full release from the faulty eating which resulted from this experience and I yield myself afresh to you so that you can be in control of my eating at all times and in all places. Amen.'

3. Go through the list of indicators of a need to find healing from past unresolved hurts, noting which ones apply to you.

4. Go through the 'Four Steps to Freedom' earlier in this chapter. Do this as often as necessary, as God brings different situations to light.

10

Mirror, Mirror on the Wall

Claire never wore *clothes*; she wore beige or grey *camouflage* – baggy trousers and loose-fitting tops which, she hoped, disguised her folds of tummy flab! When she went on the Fit For Life Forever programme, and began to change from the inside out, one of the first outward changes that others observed was that she was beginning to use brighter colours in her new wardrobe. What was happening? She was beginning to be more positive about who she was. The drab colours had not only reflected how she had previously felt about herself and life in general, but also a subconscious desire to hide from the world. Self-conscious of her shape and size, she was ashamed and just wanted to go unnoticed. And it wasn't just the way she dressed: she seldom wore make-up and paid little attention to her hair. But now, having learned about her true identity, she was becoming better groomed in every respect. It wasn't vanity; she was simply learning to love and respect herself more and desired to make the most of what her Creator had given her.

Hurts from our past, as well as hindering our relationships

with others, have a profound effect on how we relate to ourselves, leaving us with feelings of shame. While true shame occurs when we are convicted by the Holy Spirit of real sin in our lives, leading us to repentance and restoration, much of the shame that people experience is psychological and based on a lie. This lie says that we are intrinsically flawed in some way and that we can never change; it leaves us feeling trapped and hopeless and results in behaviours which only increase the sense of shame, such as bingeing on food. There goes that vicious circle again. . .

If you are a seasoned dieter, then you may well have developed surreptitious eating behaviour. Having announced that you are on a diet, your friends and family are watching everything you put into your mouth. As much as you want to lose weight you also want approval and applause for being strong-willed and resisting temptation. So what do you do? You perform well in front of your audience and then, when you are alone, you turn to your secret hoard of goodies. Just as it is guilt and shame that drive you to eat in secret, so once you have eaten, guilt and shame are compounded because you feel that you have done a very bad thing.

Shame is closely related to feelings of failure and rejection. Barbara, who attended one of our day seminars, was constantly criticised by her husband for her cooking. Feeling inadequate in this area she had resorted to ready-to-eat processed meals which were relatively easy to prepare but also helped pile on the pounds. Eating, for her, provided temporary relief from her sense of shame for being unable to satisfy her husband.

Self-image, Self-worth and Self-esteem

Although we often use these familiar terms interchange-
ably, they each have a different meaning. By *self-image* we
mean the *picture* that we have of ourselves which is based
upon our beliefs about who and what we are and of our
various abilities. Our *self-worth* is based on our self-image
and is the *value* that each of us places on our own characteristics, abilities and behaviours. Our *self-esteem* is also
based on our self-image and has to do with our *feelings*
about ourselves – our emotional response towards all that
we have done, and to what others have done to us. Clearly,
if we have a faulty self-image, then this will adversely affect
both our self-worth and our self-esteem.

If you were looking for conventional, worldly ways of
boosting your low self-esteem, then you might begin by trying to *change your image*. Having the 'right image' seems to
be of paramount importance in this day and age and there
is no shortage of books, organisations and individuals aimed
at helping you find it. I typed in 'image consultant' as a web
search and came up with more than six million locations!
And for the phrase 'Improve your self-image', I found more
than ten million site references – all there to help you project onto the world the image that you believe others will
like and respond positively to.

Are you caught in the trap of trying to find the perfect
self-image? When you can't measure up to your ideal body
image nor accept who you are, you perceive yourself as a
failure and carry the illusion that you are not good enough,
thin enough or beautiful enough.

So is emulating others really the answer? The physical

image put forward by the media is the waif-like model who weighs on average 25% less than a typical woman and who has a BMI between 15–20% lower than that which is considered healthy. One magazine reportedly spent £1,500 just for the touch-ups to a glossy photo of Claudia Schiffer. If she needed that amount of cosmetic doctoring to achieve the right image, then we might as well forget it – we'll never be able to compete!

Other approaches to improving your self-esteem might include *changing your behaviour* – learning to act the part to fit in socially. So desperate are some of us for the acceptance and approval of others that this even becomes the prime motivation to perform well in a slimming club. If you stick to the rules, if you are 'good all week', then you are likely not only to lose some weight but also to win the approval and applause of both your leaders and peers. One might argue that the end justifies the means if it helps you to perform well and achieve your weight goals, but what happens when you reach your target or eventually leave the group? Without the constant recognition and support, you begin to lose your way. All too soon the weight is replaced. Only when you are seeking to regulate your weight for yourself, or in response to the conviction of the Holy Spirit, can you expect long-term results.

One increasingly fashionable way of seeking to improve our image and thus create greater self-esteem is by *cosmetic surgery*. Once seen as the quirky privilege of the rich and famous, this has now gained acceptance among the masses and is within the pocket of many aspiring people to find a quick-fix for a lifetime of over-indulgence as well as seeking to turn back the years. I don't want to enter the debate concerning the ethics of such action, only question the possible motivation. Cosmetic surgery will, if handled by a competent consultant, improve both your looks and your self-esteem – *temporarily*. But unless your self-image and self-esteem come from *within*; unless they are based on who you are rather than what you project, then cosmetic surgery will, like food, only satisfy your need for a short while. Many who have one type of cosmetic surgery often go after more and more in their quest for what they perceive as the perfect body. It is not only expensive, but comes dangerously close, in my opinion, to an inordinate love of self which violates the first commandment: 'You shall have no other gods before Me' (Exodus 20:3).

As well as offering ways of improving our self-image through changing our image, our behaviour or our looks, another popular approach is that of *positive thinking* which ultimately aims to change both our attitudes and behaviour. Through this method a person reads aloud statements of positive affirmation concerning him- or herself. The rationale behind this is that since poor self-esteem stems from negative thinking, we can, by counteracting the negatives with positives, build up a powerful frame of reference which will enable us to believe more in ourselves and to function more successfully.

This approach comes so close to the truth, but it is still a lie. The negatives, which we have falsely come to accept as self-defining, do need to be replaced with positives, but we need to be careful that we are not just replacing one lie with another. Typical of the affirmations I have found in self-help books are statements like: 'I am getting better and better in every way', or 'my friends and family love me', or 'I attract large sums of money'. Other statements sound good but don't really say anything, like: 'the best is here for me to call into existence now', and 'I shift from a limiting mental state to a limitless mental state easily and consistently'. This kind of spurious self-convincing leads only to self-deception and is spawned by the father of lies, none other than Satan himself. A false 'positive' self-esteem is every bit as damaging as a false 'negative' one and will result in even worse bondage for those who are trapped by it, as it can lead to a self-reliance which leaves God totally out of the picture.

Our True Self-image

Positive thinking advocates cannot offer anything to compare with our true self-image which is found in God's word. Here we read that we have been made 'in the image of God' (Genesis 1:27). This does not make us 'gods' as New-agers would have us believe, but it tells us that we are related upwards to the Divine Order and not downwards to the animal kingdom, as evolutionists would assert. Sin has marred that image but it is still there, stamped irrevocably on the very core of our being. Every one of us on the face of this planet is here by God's design and each one of us has the capacity to reflect His glory. God doesn't make junk!

Furthermore, we are God's children. All of us are His by creation, but those of us who have received Christ personally into our lives by faith have also become His by adoption. In John 1:12 we read that '. . . to all who did receive Him, who believed in His name, He gave the right to become children of God. . . ' The Holy Spirit brings us to new birth and then gives us the witness within our hearts that God is our Father (Romans 8:15). When you confess, as a believer, 'I am a true child of God', you are stating the truth about your image.

Our True Self-worth

Since you and I are created by God and in His image this gives us enormous self-worth. If we were to value a painting, what would give it worth would first of all be the name of the painter. If the artist was one of the 'Great Masters' then the painting would be worth millions, whatever its aesthetic appeal. The value would also reflect the originality of the piece – something unique having greater worth than that which is commonplace. Well we have each been created by the greatest of all Masters – the Lord Himself – and each one of us is totally unique and irreplaceable.

Another way of defining the worth of the painting would be the price that a person was willing to pay in order to possess it. Sometimes we throw up our hands in horror when we learn about the price paid for some seemingly senseless 'work of art', but whatever we think about it is irrelevant – the fact that someone else was prepared to pay over the top has decided its worth. To the world, you and I might seem worthless, but this does not matter in the least. The fact is that God so loved the world that He gave His only begotten Son, Jesus, for us (John 3:16). He Himself took our sins in His body on the cross, taking the punishment we deserved, in order that we might be forgiven and received back into the bosom of the Father. It may sound 'over the top' but it's the truth!

The price that God paid in order to redeem you and me

was the blood of His innocent Son, and without that sacrifice we would all be without hope and eternally cast away from His presence. If that doesn't give us a true sense of self-worth, that nothing can! Never mind if others reject us; we are accepted by grace in the Beloved, that is in Christ, and are restored to a right relationship with Him (see Ephesians 1:6). Having been bought at such a price, we belong to Him. He has chosen to dwell within us as His Temple by His Holy Spirit and all He asks is that we glorify Him in this new creation by presenting ourselves to Him as a living sacrifice (see 1 Corinthians 6:16–20 and Romans 12:1).

We have worth simply because Christ has made us worthy. An affirmation of our true worth could be embodied, then, in this statement: 'I have worth because I am unique and am created by God. He paid the ultimate price for me in giving up His Son to die in my place.' Start to confess this on a daily basis and you will be allowing the truth to take root in your heart. This will set you free from the negatives of self-doubt and poor self-esteem.

True and False Self-love

There are two types of 'love of self' spoken of in the Bible. One is our fallen self-centred nature which is self-absorbing and narcissistic. This is the self-love which Jesus said we should deny when we take up our cross to follow Him (Matthew 16:24), and it is only at self-love's expense that we can make any spiritual progress in our Christian walk. It is this self-love which is the root of all our sin and which God passed judgement on when He sent Jesus to die in our place.

The second type of self-love is not sin: 'The Scriptures everywhere assume that an appropriate self-love, self-care, and self-appreciation is normal, and *nowhere* tells us to hate or neglect ourselves, or to indulge in self-deprecation.'[1] Jesus was speaking of this when He said: 'You shall love your neighbour as yourself' (Matthew 19:19). This kind of self-love isn't self-centred, but self-accepting. It speaks of the created self which Christ died to redeem; this is the self which, through the power of the Holy Spirit, is being restored to God's image from one degree of glory to another (2 Corinthians 3:18). When we love ourselves in this biblical way it allows us to be comfortable with who we are so that we are more able to give ourselves to others.

Secular positive thinking not only replaces a negative lie with a positive lie, it seeks to deny or excuse all that is bad within us. Guilt is seen as unhealthy and so is sidestepped to alleviate the shame. We are taught instead to blame our parents, our genes or our background for the flaws in our nature. But biblical confession has no use of such whitewash! It affirms the positives, certainly, but it also faces us up to the true negatives, not to condemn us, but so that through acknowledging our true moral guilt we may turn to Christ and receive forgiveness. We need therefore not only to affirm the positives, but to confess our sin.

Two Types of Guilt

There are two types of guilt: psychological (subjective) guilt

---

[1] Seamands, Dr David, *Healing Grace* (Wheaton, IL: Victor Books, 1988)

and moral (objective) guilt. 'Psychological guilt grows out of a shamed identity; objective guilt grows out of an honest evaluation of ourselves.'[2] Some of the shame we carry, which has caused us to turn to food in order to bury the pain, is not valid. For instance, when a woman is raped and feels dirty and ashamed, this shame is a lie which only compounds the pain of her trauma. But the shame that we carry because we have transgressed God's moral law is of a totally different order. It comes with conviction of the Holy Spirit and is the gift of God which leads us to repentance and reconciliation. Once we have repented and experience the joy of forgiveness this shame is totally removed and we have peace with God. Our Heavenly Father remembers our sin no more!

Our True Guilt Regarding Food and Eating

Throughout this book, as I have explained the various reasons why many of us turn to food, I have sought to spare you from the overbearing feelings of guilt and condemnation which diets, by their very nature, have inflicted upon you. I hope you understand by now that being overweight does not make you a bad person and that failing to reap permanent results from a diet regime does not make you a failure. Rather, such disappointing results were predictable. But there are some ways in which overeaters relate to food which *are* sin and for such behaviour it is right and proper for you to experience true guilt and shame.

I have already mentioned gluttony and greed, which

---

[2] Halliday, Judy Wardell, *Thin Again* (Lighthouse Books, 1994)

occur when your love for food turns to lust. Where these things rule in your life you have made food an idol and your refrigerator has become your shrine! If you are an emotional eater and have been covering or suppressing your emotional pain by self-medicating on food (or starvation) you have developed a dependency upon food for comfort rather than looking to God for His comfort and healing. Then, you may have tried in your own strength to overcome your weight issues, when all the time God was waiting for you to turn to Him and receive His strength which is perfected in your weakness.

Reading these things, if the cap fits, wear it, but please don't whip yourself. I had to plead guilty to all of the above, but much of my 'sin' was done in ignorance because I didn't know a better way. However, in order to be set free I have learnt to own the truth, no matter how unpalatable it is. Knowing that God loves me, no matter how much or how often I mess up, enables me to be real – real with Him and real with myself. 'There is no fear in love, but perfect love casts out fear' (1 John 4:18).

Receiving God's Forgiveness

In the last chapter I shared about how the unresolved pain in our lives not only causes us to look to food as a panacea but also how it affects our relationships with others. God's remedy for the hurts we have received from others is to forgive and I hope that, where applicable, you have already found the grace to do just that.

In several places in the New Testament the concepts of forgiving others and being forgiven ourselves are linked. As we have seen, in the Lord's Prayer Jesus tells us that we need to forgive in order to be forgiven (Matthew 6:14). God's grace has already enabled you to forgive others. How much more, then, will He be gracious to forgive you also.

So we see that there are two sides to the coin – your need to forgive others and also your need to receive forgiveness, not just from others, not just from yourself, but also from God. You may not have realised it, but your deep-seated true moral guilt and shame has also caused you to turn to food for comfort. You don't have to keep running from yourself. Own the truth and it will set you free. Here is what you should do. . .

Finding Peace With God and Peace With Yourself

Firstly, accept your guilt. Don't make excuses and don't try and hide from your true condition. Remember God loves you, warts and all, and nothing is hidden from His sight. You need to confess your sin to God alone, but if it helps you may prefer to seal what you are doing by praying in the presence of someone you trust. Now you are going to pray, but as you do, remember that God has promised that 'if we confess our sins He is faithful and just to forgive us our sins and to cleanse us from all unrighteousness' (1 John 1:9). You may pray in your own words, or you may use this prayer as a model:

> Dear God, I come to You looking for mercy. Just as I have, with Your help, forgiven those who have wronged me, I know that I, too, need to receive forgiveness from You for my own sins. I now confess to You all the wrong things I have done. I also repent of every wrong thought, word and attitude. (Here you

can be specific if you so wish – praying out loud or in your heart.) I believe that Your Son, Jesus, died on the cross, taking the penalty for my sin, so that I might be forgiven. By faith I now put my trust in Him as my Saviour, and thank You that for His sake You have heard and answered my prayer. Amen.

Growing in Your New Identity

Once you have repented of your sin and trusted Christ for forgiveness you are free from the penalty of your sin. If this has been the first time that you have prayed this kind of prayer, then you have just walked through a door into a whole new quality of life – eternal life. The Bible says in 2 Corinthians 5:17 that you have in fact become a new creation. The old has passed away and the new has come! There is now no condemnation to make you feel guilty or ashamed and God views you just as if you had never sinned. Don't look back, for God promises never to bring up your past mistakes.

In order to help you understand the way you tick and how your self-image has affected your relationship with food, this book has necessarily forced you to focus on *your* feelings, *your* hurts, *your* circumstances, but the healthiest thing you can do now is to change your focus. Get it off yourself and onto God. Your self-confidence will grow, not as you look inward, but as you look upwards. Learn to affirm the truth of who you are in God and who He is in you.

One of your reasons for overeating has been your own self-loathing, but now, just as God has forgiven and accepted you, you need to forgive and accept yourself. 'Let the peace of Christ rule in your hearts,' the Bible says (Colossians

3:15). Peace comes as you accept God's forgiveness, and learn that He really does love you unconditionally and permanently just as you are. When you stand in front of your mirror and are tempted to reject the image you see, learn to respond by telling yourself how beautiful you are in God's eyes. Once I understood these principles I would look at my still-obese form in the mirror and say, 'I'm not fat, I'm a slim person in recovery!' You see, on the inside I was already slim, but my outward form just hadn't caught up yet.

These lessons are not absorbed overnight. The negative voices you have listened to for years will not be silenced immediately, but every time you find yourself thinking in the old, unhelpful, deceiving ways, just turn to the truth of God's word and use it as a sword in your hand to defeat the devil (Ephesians 6:16–17). The more you confess the truth of who you are in Christ, so your negative self-image will diminish and, as it does, so the need to comfort eat will also reduce until it no longer has any pull on you at all.

Home Assignments

1. Write down how you honestly feel about yourself? Your looks, your personality and character and your achievements and contribution to society.

2. How do you feel that others – your family, your friends and your work associates – view you?

3. How real are you with other people? Do you: (a) Tell people what you think they want to hear? (b) Seek to project an image acceptable to your group? (c) Admit to your weaknesses and fears? (d) Try to please others?

4. What do you think would happen if you let people see the 'real you'?

5. Now write down, in personal terms, how God sees you and your worth to Him. Read this out three times: once to yourself, once as thanksgiving to God, and once to the devil to let him know that you know who you are!

6. Review Chapters 4–10, which have covered many reasons for inappropriate eating behaviour. Now use the Reasons For Eating Log in Appendix 3 to try and identify all these different reasons as they occur in your daily life. Follow the example given as a guide and for several days keep a record of when you eat outside of your main mealtimes. What are you discovering about your relationship with food and eating?

11

An Introduction to Awareness Eating

When you began to read this book you were probably itching to get on with the nitty-gritty of learning how to lose weight without dieting, but to have provided this information *before* explaining the many reasons why so many of us eat when we are not physiologically hungry would have been to put the cart before the horse. Knowing technically what to do and yet lacking the ability to carry it through would only have left you frustrated, sabotaging your own efforts without understanding why. Now that you are beginning to deal with the roots of your disordered eating you can begin, with God's help, to build upon a firmer foundation.

If you have completed the Meal Observation Log from Appendix 1 then you have already started to experience awareness eating, and you probably had a few surprises about how you have been relating to food. Maybe you discovered that you are a grazer – eating one thing after another between meals. Perhaps you realised that you were eating when you weren't in fact hungry, or that you ate more than you truly needed. And what about the whole meal experience? Did you find yourself eating food that you didn't altogether enjoy, or find that the atmosphere of your eating environment gave you negative feelings of stress, rush and distraction?

You are going to learn, in this chapter, just how important all these factors are in producing a healthy relationship with food – one in which you are fully in control and making the right choices in respect to your own goals.

But first I want you to think about some people you know who have never had a problem regarding weight. You know the ones I mean – they're the ones who happily tuck into all kinds of food that you're longing to be able to enjoy but daren't for fear of piling on the pounds. They've never been to a slimming club or been on a diet. They've worn the same size clothes for years and they can't seem to get their heads round why eating should be such a problem for you. And when you ask them what they do in order to stay so slim, they haven't a clue. What's more they often don't even seem to stick to any 'good eating habits' and may not even eat healthily by any defined standards. Ask these people if they've ever put weight on, and they will usually say no. Or perhaps they might confess to a nagging concern that they've put on a couple of pounds over the last five years and would like to shed them. 'A couple of pounds!' you think to yourself, 'in five years!' You know quite well, that for you it's easy to put on a couple of stone in five months. What you would give to have a problem like theirs!

So what is their secret? Is it just a matter of them being blessed with a highly effective metabolism while we appear to have been cursed by some 'fat gene' – whatever that is!

Well, undoubtedly genetics do play a role, as we discussed earlier, but it is certainly not the whole answer.

I have a friend, Gilly, an ex-schoolteacher, who fits this 'forever slim' category. So I quizzed her intensely to try and find out precisely how she related to food. Here is a transcript of that interview:

Me: So, tell me, Gilly, how do you keep so slim? Are there any foods which you avoid?

Gilly: No, nothing! I eat absolutely what I enjoy. There are some foods that I don't eat, but that's just because I don't like them.

Me: But do you follow any kind of regime – counting calories, eating different food types in certain ratios, or anything like that?

Gilly: Not at all. I think that I do maintain a fairly healthy diet overall, but that's because I like healthier food, not because I feel I must eat it.

Me: What about mealtimes? Do you always eat three meals a day, and do you always have breakfast?

Gilly: I would usually eat breakfast, especially when I was teaching because it was such a demanding job, and I generally just have a small snack for lunch – unless I'm really hungry. We usually eat our main meal in the evening, but we don't have any rule about all this. If I were going out for dinner in the evening then I probably would eat very lightly throughout the rest of the day, but enough not to make me feel hungry around teatime, because if I ate then I wouldn't be ready for the meal. And if I'd eaten out late, then I most probably wouldn't need breakfast the following day. Since that would usually be the weekend it wouldn't matter at all.

Me: Let's talk some more about eating out. Many restaurants serve large portions of food these days. Do you try and clear your plate, even if you are feeling full?

Gilly: Never! I hate the feeling of being overfull and it would spoil my evening to stuff myself, so no, I'd never do that.

Me: So does that mean that you usually don't have a dessert?

Gilly: Sometimes I do and sometimes I don't. If I fancy a dessert then I make sure that I have left room for it, even if it means leaving a part of the meal.

Me: Don't you ever feel that you've wasted your money, leaving food?

Gilly: I don't like it, but it's better than feeling bloated or cheated when I've gone out to enjoy myself.

Me: Do you eat between meals?

Gilly: If I'm hungry I might have a piece of fruit or something, but generally not.

Me: What about work? When other staff members bring in cakes or something as a birthday treat, what do you do then?

Gilly: I'd probably say, 'Thank you very much. Do you think I could keep it to eat later?'

Me: And then you'd eat it with your lunch, right?

Gilly: Or instead of my lunch. I probably wouldn't need both, but I could take it home and enjoy it with my supper, providing that I'd left room for it.

Me: So what about eating at home? Do you always clean your plate?

Gilly: Well, I can generally gauge how much I need and don't give myself more than I expect to eat. But if I found that I was feeling full, then I'd definitely leave it.

Me: What about your upbringing? Did your parents ever make you eat up before you were allowed to leave the table?
Gilly: I can't remember. Probably not.
Me: And what about your own children? Did you ever insist that they ate up everything you'd given them?
Gilly: If it was something they said they didn't like, then I'd encourage them to try some, but if they said they were full I never insisted that they eat more.
Me: A lot of people tend to eat when they're feeling low or upset. Do you ever use food for comfort?
Gilly: No, in fact being upset has the opposite effect for me. I find it hard to eat under such circumstances.
Me: Thank you, Gilly. Your answers have been both interesting and enlightening.

***

You might like to ask your ever-slim friends the same questions. What you will probably find, as I did with Gilly, is that these people *only* eat to fulfil their physiological hunger. They do not (as we have been finding) use food to feed their minds or their hearts. They are not enslaved to any diet regimes or food and eating mantras, neither do they turn to food to help them cope with pain and stress.

If only we could learn to do the same. . . and that, basically, is what Fit for Life Forever and this book is all about – learning to eat intuitively, in a natural way.

So, now you are about to be set free! Fit for Life Forever follows four basic life principles (not rules) which are designed to help you eat intuitively again, obeying your body's natural instincts and liberating you forever from the curse of dieting. These will be addressed fully in subsequent chapters but for now, here they are in outline.

The Four Principles

1. *Eat when you are truly hungry.* You will learn to wait until your body signals that you are in need of food. This will involve recognising and unlearning many false and unhelpful beliefs that you have hitherto maintained, so that you can once again experience the sensations in your body which are God-given and which speak directly to your individual physiological need.

2. *Stop eating when you are satisfied.* There is a difference between being 'satisfied' and being 'full up', just as there is also a difference between being 'full' and being 'stuffed to bursting point'. You are going to learn how to recognise this point of optimum satisfaction and acquire the necessary skills so that you do not abuse your body by feeding it more than it wants or needs. You will be freed from the guilt feelings which cause you to have to consume every last bit of food on your plate and the crazy notion that by eating all we can we are gaining value for money!

3. *Eat in total freedom, but with responsibility.* Did you ever hear of a diet which could offer you *total* freedom? Isn't it true that diet food is generally unappetising and bland? And haven't we been told that eating certain foods is 'good' or 'righteous' while to eat others is 'bad'? In future you will experience the freedom of being able to eat whatever you like. As has already been observed, the deprivation factor of

most diets incites within us an accentuated desire for what we feel we can't have. By giving yourself permission to eat what you like, you will find in a very short period of time that you actually don't want or crave those 'forbidden fruits' any more, and your body will start to tell you what it needs in order to receive its necessary nutrients. Along with this freedom, you will find as you start to take control of your life, that there will come a new respect for your own body and you will not want to abuse it by feeding it a load of low-nutrient / high-calorie food. So this is not a 'carte blanche' to give in to all your passions and cravings regarding food, but a path where freedom and responsibility walk hand in hand.

4. *Eat consciously in an atmosphere conducive to all-round satisfaction.* Before we can start to eat intuitively, or naturally, we have to learn to eat consciously. We need to take an analytical view of our eating habits and observe our behaviour regarding food, for only then can we see what is working for us and what is working against us. Only then can we start to bring about the changes which are necessary to ensure that we don't overeat. When we eat in a non-focused way we tend to be on autopilot, shovelling down our food and hardly being aware of anything we've eaten. But when we make the food central to our eating it has the capacity to enhance our enjoyment, not just physically but also mentally and emotionally, so that we leave the table fully satisfied and less likely to be looking around for something else to eat within minutes!

So there you have it! It isn't complicated, is it? In fact it really is just common sense. You may have been searching for years for that elusive diet which would enable you to regulate your eating in such a way that you would be able to consume just the right amount of calories or just the right balance of certain foods without hating every minute of it. You are weary of the constant battle, but even now you have been bracing yourself for the worst – expecting to be told a whole string of 'dos and don'ts'. To your surprise (and maybe disbelief) you have, instead, been handed a set of keys and told to go and let yourself out of prison!

You hold the keys gingerly in your hands. But the gift, while filling you with new-found hope, also evokes a degree of apprehension. 'What if I can't find the way?' you might say, or, 'What if the keys won't turn in the locks?' You might also suddenly find yourself asking whether you really want such freedom, with all the personal responsibility it entails. We have all heard of those career criminals who have been instituted for so long that the life behind bars, while regimented and restricted, does offer a degree of security and becomes, for them, preferable to having to cope with freedom outside. Perhaps this is you?

These are all valid questions, but in response to them all I would simply say, 'What have you got to lose?' Nothing – except unwanted weight! And you have everything to gain. Sure, you may find that some of the locks are a bit stiff. Don't worry! In the next chapter you are going to find out why this is and where you can find the oil which will release them.

Home Assignments

1. If you did not complete the Meal Observation Log in Appendix 1, do it now. Even if you did complete this

chart, you may like to repeat the exercise to see if things have already begun to change.

2. If you know people who are 'naturally slim', interview them along the same lines as the dialogue you have just read between Gilly and myself. Compare the answers.

12

Finding Hungry and Finding Full

One of the most universally accepted food mantras that we hear these days is that we should eat regular meals. This is usually taken to mean that we should eat at least three times a day. To skip breakfast, we are told, is really bad for us because we need food to kick-start our metabolism, while to eat late at night is bad for us, as the body is not as efficient in the evening and night-time hours to use up the calories. We are also told that if we miss a meal we are more likely to binge on fatty, sugary snacks and so gain weight. So let's examine these suppositions, looking at the research which has taken place in these various fields.

What about eating three square meals a day? This food mantra was pretty much the only approach to eating in the 1940s and earlier. Helen Andrews, a nutrition scientist at the British Nutrition Foundation, commenting on this approach, has written that historically:

all meals were substantial and the average calorie intake was higher than it is today, but people were much more active. Very few people would skip breakfast, lunch or dinner and snacking between meals was unheard of. There is nothing wrong with this approach, other than it is simply not practical for most modern lifestyles.[1]

Karen Collins, MS, RD, CDN, with the American Institute for Cancer Research, concluded from various studies that 'eating frequency has no effect on a person's overall metabolic rate.'[2] This view is supported by Vicki Sullivan, PhD, RD, LD, national lecturer and president of Balance, LLC. She writes: 'The only thing that has been consistently shown to increase BMR (Basal Metabolic Rate) is exercise.'[3]

Some nutritionists advocate eating up to six small meals a day, as opposed to fewer, larger ones. Professor Andrew Prentice of the Medical Research Council's international nutrition group believes that little and often is a good approach to eating. 'Metabolically, it looks as though regular nibbling is a good way to do things,' he says. 'It puts less strain on the body if you are not taking in too much food all at once.'[4] To a point Karen Collins agrees with this, conceding that, since everyone is different, 'eating every three hours would certainly help some people control appetite and feel more energized.'[5]

However, it has to be said that the more times a day you sit down to eat a meal or snack, the more opportunities you have to overeat! If you happen to be someone who has difficulty stopping once you get started, or who regularly

---

[1] Andrews, Helen quoted by Hoe, Lucie, in 'You Are When You Eat', in *The Daily Telegraph* (19/09/05)

[2] Collins, Karen, ibid.

[3] Sullivan, Vicki, ibid.

[4] Prentice, Professor Andrew, ibid.

[5] Collins, Karen, ibid.

eats for non-physiological reasons, then it's quite possible that, for you, eating five or six times a day is a recipe for disaster. But if you truly can regulate your eating to your body's physiological need, then a pattern of three meals a day does work for a lot of people.

What about breakfast? Are we more likely to gain weight if we skip this meal? The Better Health TV Channel recently carried out a survey which showed that one third of adults regularly skip breakfast and that this trend is increasing.[6] There are many studies around that claim that by skipping breakfast we are more likely to binge on high-calorie, low-nutrient foods later. But a closer look at why most people skip breakfast seems to have nothing at all to do with hunger levels. According to the Better Health TV Channel, here are some of the main reasons which were given:

- Not enough time
- Too tired to bother
- Wanting to spend the extra time dozing in bed
- No readily available breakfast foods in the house

In all of these cases breakfast was being skipped as a matter of convenience and not hunger. This being the case, one could certainly expect hunger to set in at a time when the most *convenient* food at hand would be a high-calorie, low-nutrient snack. Of course, under such circumstances, the fears of bingeing on inappropriate food are well founded. But the problem here isn't going without breakfast; rather it is a lackadaisical attitude to eating in general. Many of us

---

[6] 'Breakfast', on Better Health TV Channel (Australia), in consultation with Deakin University

will wake up relatively hungry, especially if we have eaten a light meal the night before, but this cannot be applied universally. The commonsense approach, for adults anyway, is to make reasoned choices and let hunger be our guide. There may be medical reasons for needing to eat at specified times – if this is the case do not go against your doctor's advice.

To me the main advantage of having breakfast is its nutritional content. Breakfast can provide a significant proportion of the day's total nutrient intake and offers the opportunity to eat some of those healthy foods we are encouraged to have several servings of every day, like fruit, whole grains, and low-fat dairy produce, as well as those foods fortified with nutrients such as iron, B vitamins and fibre. One healthy solution for those who are not ready to eat breakfast first thing in the morning is to plan similar foods into their first meal of the day, whenever that happens to be.

Weight loss ultimately is not governed by how often or how regularly we eat but how much energy (or calories) is consumed in relation to our energy expenditure, and the best way to ensure that we only consume what we need is to learn how to listen to our body's hunger and satisfaction signals, which is what this chapter is going to teach you. All things being equal there may well be some health advantages to eating small amounts of food at regular intervals, or not eating too late at night, or for starting the day with a healthy breakfast; but whatever advantages there are, these are outweighed by the foolishness of eating if our bodies are not ready for it. For instance, if we eat a substantial evening meal, say between 7–8pm, followed by a relaxed evening in front of the television, then there is a strong likelihood that, come early morning, we may not yet be hungry. To eat breakfast simply out of a legalistic compliance to a food mantra is simply overloading the body with unwanted calories. It may keep the body's metabolism burning, but you will still gain weight if the food you eat is surplus to requirements. When the Fit For Life Forever principles are applied, which focus on eating in response to our body's hunger and satisfaction signals, then such regulatory advice is unnecessary and may, in fact, be counter-productive.

If we do not learn to become conscious eaters, aware of our own body's needs, then all we have left to guide us is a set of legalistic rules and regulations. But when we learn to submit our appetites to God, to listen to our bodies and to let the Holy Spirit be our guide, then we can trust the inner voice which will cause us to eat responsibly without abusing or neglecting ourselves.

Hunger

The first thing that we need to learn is to recognise real hunger. I wonder if you truly know what this is? I don't mean starving, as in a famine situation where people might not be able to eat adequately for weeks, but just plain hungry – ready for the next meal. This isn't such a ridiculous question as it might at first appear. After all, some of you reading this book may say that you are *always* hungry, that this is the crux of the problem.

Most overweight people, when they say they are hungry, often only *think* they are. Perhaps they are responding to a clock and not their bodies, sometimes they are just bored and need something to do, or they feel a bit of a rumble in their intestines and conclude, quite falsely in many cases, that they must need something to eat. You may hear yourself saying that you 'just fancy something nice', but this is mouth hunger, not physical hunger and its source is in the senses or the imagination. Sometimes the hunger pain we feel emanates from our heart and then it is deep-seated inner hunger we need to address, not our stomachs.

Medical Causes of Hunger and Obesity

From a medical standpoint there are a few conditions which do increase hunger. Two examples of this are a disease called Prader-Willi syndrome, a genetic disorder in which sufferers are totally unable to discern when they are full (but this is extremely rare), and a malfunctioning thyroid. Another thing to take into account is the effect of various types of medication on hunger levels. These are: steroids, anti-depressants, some painkillers and some forms of the contraceptive pill. If you think that your weight is affected by medication, then by all means talk to your doctor to see if there are alternative medications that could be prescribed which will not affect your perceived hunger in this way. If you have diabetes, you may well have a resistance to insulin which can also affect your blood sugar levels and feelings of hunger. These problems may present a greater challenge to your applying the principles I am about to describe, but with God's help you will still be able to succeed.

The purpose of this chapter is to learn how to listen to your body and to recognise its true hunger and satisfaction signals, but first let us define our terms:

- *Hunger* is a normal sensation that makes you want to eat. It is controlled by a region of your brain called the hypothalamus, your blood sugar (glucose) level, how empty your stomach and intestines are, and certain hormone levels in your body. More about this in a minute.
- *Satiety (or satisfaction)* is a feeling of fullness and satisfaction. Stretch receptors in the stomach send signals to the brain that the stomach is filled. Other contributory factors are increased blood sugar (glucose), the activity of the hypothalamus, and the presence of food in the intestines.

Our Bodies' Hunger and Satisfaction Signals

When God designed our bodies He took into full account all of our physiological needs, and so that we wouldn't abuse or neglect them, He set within us various physiological signals that would indicate when and how our needs should be met. A good example of this is our need for sleep. We all know very well how our bodies indicate to us that we are getting tired: the eyelids become heavy and we start to yawn and lose concentration. Similarly, our bodies' sensations tell us when we need to relieve ourselves, which is just as well, as to ignore these signals could prove quite embarrassing!

Well, God has also set within our bodies hunger signals to tell us when it is time for us to eat and, in a simplified way, it works like this: when our energy levels begin to run low, a message is sent to the hypothalamus gland in the brain which in turn sends a signal to the stomach to begin to prepare itself for receiving food. In order to properly digest our food acid is needed and it is this that begins to build up in our stomachs when we are hungry, giving us a hollow sensation which we correctly interpret as hunger. It is further stimulated by the senses. Similarly, once hunger is satisfied, a message is sent to the hypothalamus to indicate that it is time to stop eating, but it normally takes around 20 minutes from the commencement of a meal in order to register, so eating quickly may cause us to consume more than we need without knowing it.

Hunger signals will vary from person to person, so you will need to acquaint yourself with your personal indicators. Emptiness, as I have described it above, is a main indicator for most people, but for some it may be a sense of faintness or dizziness, or irritability or a feeling of nausea or headache. The problem with these other signals is that they can, so often, indicate other conditions and not just hunger, so they are perhaps not so reliable. But in a short time you will come to understand your own body, and as you work with its natural rhythms, not against them by artificially imposed feeding times, you will begin to feel both liberated and in control.

How the Art of 'Listening' is Lost

A newborn baby needs only a few basic needs to be met in order to feel content. So long as it is well fed, clean and secure, then that is all that matters. Basically, the newborn baby will wake up when needing to be fed or changed and once the need is met will happily drop off to sleep again, often cradled in its mother's arms.

But unfortunately for the mother, the baby can make

demands to be fed at the most inconvenient moments: the middle of the night, daytime while there's shopping to be done, or evening when it would be good to go out for an hour or two for a change and leave baby with Grandma or some other responsible adult. This isn't insurmountable if mother is bottle-feeding the baby but can be a major headache if she is breastfeeding. So very soon baby is introduced to the idea of routine, which certainly does have its good points. After all, believing that one can have just what one wants the moment a yell is sent up can prove to be a recipe for major problems further down the line.

From the point of view of food consumption, however, what we have done, in introducing the idea of regular mealtimes, is begin a process whereby the body's natural hunger signals are being overridden by external controls. In time it isn't our bodies that tell us when we are hungry, but the clock.

As we continued to grow, in order to fit in with family and cultural expectations, we learnt to override our hunger signals. We learnt that there were times when, hungry or not, we would be expected to wait until 'dinnertime' or 'teatime' in order to eat, and we learnt that when it was mealtime we ate along with everybody else, even if we weren't yet really hungry. Perhaps, too, when we were full we were told that we could not leave the table until we had eaten up and cleaned our plate.

It may have been that you were told that you couldn't have your dessert until you had finished the main course – after all, what child wouldn't opt to have chocolate or ice-cream before vegetables! There is some good nutritional sense in this approach, except that when too much food has been offered in the first place, the child (who may have instinctively left room for the sweet course) is likely to overeat the main course, just so that he or she can continue to overeat some more in the form of the pudding afterwards. This adds insult to injury.

By the time we reach adulthood we have been taught and conditioned so much regarding food that many of us no longer know what it means to be hungry, neither do we know what it means to be satisfied. Instead our eating habits are governed by a whole string of social niceties and taboos, cultural norms, heavily imprinted messages received from our parents and teachers and the demands of our fickle emotions. When we look to some diet to try and sort out the mess that we have got ourselves into we generally, and unwittingly, exacerbate the problem by simply adding more rules and restrictions to our already tortured lives.

On top of this, many of us as children were introduced to the idea of sweet food being given as a bribe or reward, or withheld as a punishment. A child may learn that by kicking up a fuss he or she will be given some sweets to keep quiet. Perhaps, when a certain task has to be done, an adult may offer something nice to eat either as a bribe or as a 'thank you' for complying. Again, when a child falls over and hurts himself, a cuddle helps take away the pain, but a handy sweet may seem to be the perfect answer to stop the tears and redirect attention!

With all of these factors coming into play, is it any wonder that our God-given hunger and satisfaction signals are ignored? By the time our children have gone through the school system, they may have learnt to expect snacks in the mid-morning and mid-afternoon as well as the three stan-dard meals of breakfast, lunch and tea. On top of this, a good number of children will head straight for the biscuit tin or a packet of crisps the minute they arrive home and will eat junk food snacks while watching TV before going to bed. This gives a total of seven eating occasions in a day! Is it any wonder that many people don't really know what it is to be hungry? They never give their bodies time to reach the point of physiological hunger before stocking up again. No wonder a quarter of the British adult population is now considered obese and that childhood obesity and type II dia-betes in young people is on the increase.

Sometimes we think that we are hungry, when actually we are just thirsty. Thirst is experienced in our mouth and throat so sometimes people confuse the two. When you think that you might be feeling hungry, but know that it really isn't that long since you last ate, try having a non-sugary drink (water is good) and see if that takes the sensa-tion away. If you are thirsty, then eating won't satisfy your need and you will carry on looking around for something else until you hit it right.

Influence of Food Type on Hunger

The problem regarding the confusion of our bodily signals, is found not only in the *amount* of food that we consume, but also in the *type*. We now understand that certain carbo-hydrate foods cause our blood sugar to rise steeply, giving us a rush of energy, only to crash again just as steeply after just a short period of time, leaving us feeling faint, irritable and . . . yes, hungry! A diet which is high in processed foods and containing large quantities of sugars, refined flour and starch, will almost certainly produce this effect in our bodies.

So let's say, for instance, that breakfast consists of a refined, flaky breakfast cereal, white toast and jam and sweet tea. All of these foods consist largely of refined carbohydrates which affect our blood sugar in the way outlined above. Not surprisingly, by mid-morning, the blood sugar levels have plummeted and there is a need for something to fill the gap before lunch. If the snack food we choose is one high in refined carbohydrates, then the extreme swing in blood sugar levels is repeated, so that by lunchtime we feel ravenous again. A lunch consisting of a French baguette, possibly with a high-carbohydrate filling, or pizza, pie or chips will again cause a rapid rise in the blood sugar. Add to this the probability of having a sugary soda to drink (a can has, on average, five teaspoons of sugar) and the body is on a carbohydrate overload. By mid-afternoon, energy levels are again flagging and another sugary snack is consumed to keep us going until the evening meal. With our modern, hectic lifestyles there often isn't time to prepare a meal from scratch, so a ready meal is quickly thrown into the microwave or oven, or a take-away is ordered and once again we are eating foods which have lots of hidden sugars and starches. Whether by hunger or habit, this is often not the end of the eating saga for the day; many will feel the need for some supper before going to bed, and this, so often, turns out to be more of the same – more starch and more sugar, in sum more refined carbohydrates.

The Glycaemic Index

What I have been alluding to, in discussing the relative effect of various foods on our blood sugar, is the Glycaemic Index (GI). Carbohydrate foods which break down quickly during digestion are said to have a high Glycaemic Index because they have an immediate and extreme effect on the blood sugar or glucose levels in our blood. Conversely, carbohydrate foods which break down slowly, thereby releasing blood sugar in a gradual, more tempered way, are said to have a low GI (see Figure 4). The highest GI is that of pure glucose, which has a ranking of 100, and all other carbohydrates are ranked on a scale of 0–100, according to their relative effect on blood sugar levels.

Low GI foods, such as whole grains, vegetables and

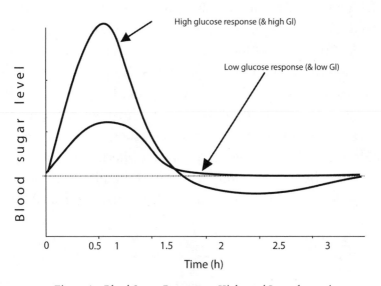

Figure 4 – Blood Sugar Response to High- and Low-glycaemic Carbohydrates

pulses are generally more satisfying than high GI foods, that is, they leave us feeling fuller for longer. Also low GI foods lower insulin levels, which is obviously beneficial for people with type II adult onset diabetes. But the good news for people needing to lose weight is that lower insulin levels also cause fat to be more easily burned, so it is less likely to be stored in the body as fat tissue. One of the recommendations given by the World Health Organisation / Food and Agriculture Organisation in 1998 was that the bulk of foods containing carbohydrates should be 'those rich in non-starch polysaccharides (dietary fibre) and with a low Glycaemic Index'.[7]

Here is a list of some common foods with a high Glycaemic Index. You will notice that many of them are the kinds of food that we use for quick snacks or packed lunches. Although many of these foods – especially those with added fats – are also high in calories, this is not the focus of the issue here. I simply want to raise your awareness of the kinds of foods which are proven to have a see-saw effect on your blood sugar levels and which therefore may cause you to feel hungry when your body is not yet in need of more food. However, when a high-glycaemic food is eaten together with low-glycaemic foods, proteins or fats, this does reduce the overall glycaemic effect. You will then not experience the same dramatic rise and fall of blood sugar levels and you are more likely to remain satisfied for longer.

---

[7] World Health Organisation/Food and Agriculture Organisation website: www.fao.org (accessed 28/11/06)

High-glycaemic Foods

Product	GI	Product	GI
White rice, steamed	98	French fries	75
French baguette	95	White bread	70
Baked / jacket potato	85	Biscuits	65
Corn flakes	84	Table sugar	64
Sweet confectionary	80	Cola drink	63
Cream crackers	78	Ice-cream	61
Doughnut with sugar	76	Pizza	60

Basically, any carbohydrate with a GI over 60 should be considered high. By comparison, here are some foods which have a moderate to low GI and which therefore do not create dramatic highs and lows in the body's blood sugar levels.

Low-glycaemic Foods

Product	GI	Product	GI
Peanuts	14	Milk chocolate	49
Many fruits	20–40	Mixed-grain bread	49
(not banana)		Strawberry jam	52
Salad foods	low	Porridge oats	53
Many vegetables	low	Basmati, brown	55
Most beans	25–48	and wild rice	
Pasta	41	Popcorn	55
		Muesli	56

Learning to Recognise 'Hungry'

It is vital in order to implement the principles of Fit For Life Forever that you learn to recognise your body's *true* hunger signals. We have already seen how, for many of us, waiting for these signals has been overridden by social conditioning, emotional eating and erratic blood sugar levels, so this is not something that you will get right overnight. Rigid dieting or fasting, where hunger is persistently denied, may affect our ability to recognise its gentle sensation; so too may the use of calorie-free drinks which can quell or avert hunger pangs, tricking us into a false sense of fullness.

One practical way of assessing your hunger levels is to view your stomach as a car fuel tank, or rather a car with a reserve tank as well. If the main tank is full, then excess fuel is stored in the reserve tank, and similarly when the main tank runs empty, fuel can be drawn from this reserve tank to meet the need. Our body fat is like the reserve tank but unfortunately it has no limits! Instead it will just continue to grow the more 'surplus to need' fuel it receives! Using the analogy of a car fuel tank, a prudent and efficient way of regulating the supply and demand is to wait until the needle on the gauge begins to hit the red band and then refuel.

Look at Figure 5, below. What you should be aiming at is to eat when your stomach is at '0' and to stop eating when you are satisfied, but not feeling stuffed! This is the point marked 'S'. Try to eat when you are truly hungry but not so hungry that you are at risk of overeating or being out of control. What I am suggesting is that you wait until your stomach feels definitely empty; but once you feel this, don't go more than an hour without eating or you will move

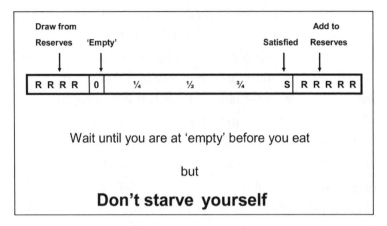

Figure 5 – Your Stomach as a Fuel Tank

beyond being truly hungry to feeling ravenous and be in danger of overeating out of a sense of deprivation. The problem with many of us who have been or still are overweight, is that we have habitually refuelled when the tank was still half full, but eaten the equivalent of a full tank's worth of fuel all the same!

Some overweight people are afraid of the hungry feeling and so eat every time they just feel 'slightly' hungry, but this, too, is likely to result in overeating. Ask yourself these questions before a meal if you aren't sure:

1. Am I hungry? (If you are unsure, wait 20 minutes and then ask yourself again.)
2. When was the last time I ate? (If it's less than three hours ago, it is probably not real hunger.)

If you recognise that you are truly hungry, but it is not a convenient time to prepare or eat a full meal, then you could eat a small healthy snack to tide you over until the next meal. Just one small piece of fruit, half a cereal bar or a cheese string will probably suffice for this.

Just as long as you are eating between the '0' mark and 'S' you *will* be drawing from your fat reserves and losing weight. If you are not sure how these benchmarks tally with your personal eating habits then try to remember if there was a time when you really had to go without food for longer than usual – perhaps you were fasting either in preparation for a blood test or for some spiritual reason. This would be less than '0' – a point where you do not want to go (except as directed by the Holy Spirit) as it may cause you to binge. Then think of a time when you really stuffed yourself with food. Perhaps it was a Christmas dinner or an 'eat-all-you-can' buffet. This is beyond 'S' and if you eat to this point, you *will* put weight on! Once you have established these parameters you can start to familiarise yourself with various points on the fuel gauge and how it feels inside your own body. Remember that although this is a physiological exercise it is still purely subjective, so don't worry if you feel the need to eat more or less often than others. It isn't about set times. Sometimes you may feel the need to eat only once a day and at other times you may want to eat several times, but so long as you are eating within your own set points of hunger and satisfaction your body will metabolise your food efficiently and you will reduce your weight until you reach your personal 'set point' which will depend upon your genetic make-up.

So When Am I Full?

We have already talked about the feeling of true physiological hunger, but what about the feeling of being full. Here are some signs you can look for. First of all you will have a feeling of satisfaction but won't feel bloated, secondly you will feel refreshed and energised, and thirdly the food itself will begin to lose its appeal.

Beyond this, the signs that you have overeaten will be if:

• You need to loosen your belt!
• You feel bloated and uncomfortable sitting down.
• You feel sleepy. (The blood cells in the brain 'shut down' in order to concentrate their efforts on digestion.)

The size of a normal empty stomach is about six inches (15 cm) long and holds about one litre capacity. However, since the stomach is a muscle, it has the capacity to respond to increased demands of both solids and fluids by increasing in size, and many obese people do have stomachs which are regularly distended to hold large amounts of food, sometimes as much as four litres at a time. You can tell if your stomach has stretched by assessing how uncomfortable you feel after consuming a large quantity of food in one sitting. Even when stomach stapling has been carried out to limit the stomach capacity, this is only a temporary measure, for even the small, surgically restricted stomach can, in time, expand considerably.

If you have habitually abused your stomach through over-extending it, led a chaotic lifestyle or tried to regulate your eating by following externally imposed diet plans, you may find it difficult at first to recognise fullness and will need to redevelop your sensitivity in this area. Meredith Luce, an American dietician who trains people to eat small portions and thus reduce their stomach size says, 'People with stretched stomachs have constantly overridden that naturally full feeling, so they are no longer sensitive to the threshold and there is nothing to stop them from overeating.'[8] This being the case, it may be (especially if you are very obese) that assessing when you are satisfied will prove quite difficult initially. But gradually, as you consistently refuse to push your stomach to its limits, it will begin to reduce its size and become a more accurate indicator. One dietician I read of seeks to help people who can't recognise their full signals by only permitting them to eat 76 bites of food a day. While I instinctively shy away from this legalistic, directive approach as a life habit, I concede that it may help initially for those who are morbidly obese, allowing time for the stomach to shrink and for sensitivity to increase.

Key to this whole process is to eat slowly and consciously and to chew your food well. This is because chewing itself sends a signal to the brain that eating is in progress and helps to release the satisfied feeling. If you bolt your food down quickly, you are more likely to overeat than if you savour each bite and eat slowly. Do not automatically eat everything on your plate, but stop and put your fork down at regular intervals and ask yourself, 'Am I still hungry, or am I satisfied?' If you are not sure, then wait a while. As you eat, enjoy every mouthful, concentrating on the various tastes, smells and textures. This way, when your body starts to signal that you are full, you will be ready to stop eating. If you eat without really thinking about what you are doing, you may well still feel a need to carry on eating,

---

[8] Luce, Meredith, quoted by Brown, Sally, in 'Shrink To Fit', *The Sunday Times* magazine (29/08/04)

not because you are still hungry but because, for true satisfaction, you need to consciously relish taste sensations in your mouth. All this will take practice, so be patient, pray and trust God. He is on your side and will help you to understand the mysterious workings of your body as you work with Him to accomplish your weight goals.

Please remember that following your body's hunger and satisfaction signals is a principle, not a law. It is a good principle and the more you are able to observe it, the more likely you are to arrive at a body weight which is right for you. But if you simply replace the laws of dieting with 'Thou shalt only eat when hungry,' and, 'Thou must stop when satisfied,' you will still be in bondage and feel guilty every time you eat a minute too early or consume one mouthful too much! Deep down you will know whether you are choosing the sensible option or just making excuses. For instance, if I was offered a slice of birthday cake which I hadn't anticipated, and I was not really hungry, I would probably still eat some in order to be a collective part of the celebration – and I'd enjoy it!

Making the Principles 'Workable'

It may be that as you have followed the logic of eating in response to your hunger and satisfaction signals, you will be thinking: 'That's all very well, but I can't just eat when I'm ready to. I have a job that requires me to take pre-arranged lunch breaks; I have a family to consider and can't have everyone eating at different times. How can I make this work?'

This is a valid question, so let me say from the outset that

I am not necessarily expecting you to make dramatic changes in your lifestyle. If I asked you to do that I would be imposing my own regime and you would probably give up in frustration. Fit For Life Forever is not about legalism, it is about developing a whole new relationship with food. Eating is a social occasion and, of course, you will want to eat with others, especially members of your own family, so let's see how you can do this and still listen to your body.

Initially you will have to make some sacrifices and, yes, eat at a different time from others if necessary. Only by allowing yourself the freedom to eat just when you are hungry can you learn to recognise your body's signals. For this reason I suggest that you begin to apply these principles at a weekend or some time when you don't have to think too much about fitting in with work schedules. You can explain to your family that for a short period you want to be able to wait until you are truly hungry and that you don't really know when this will occur. Ask for their understanding, patience and support and explain that it will not last for long. If you are the household food provider, you will need to provide food for others at their usual time, unless, of course, you all decide to apply these principles together! This would be fantastic, but you will need to prepare the kinds of meals that can be individually heated up in the microwave, so that everyone can eat when they are truly hungry. If it happens that you have prepared a meal for your family and you know that you, yourself, are not yet ready to eat, you may need to go and do something else while they eat, in order not to be tempted to eat when you are not yet physiologically hungry! Once you know in general how long it takes for the hungry feeling to develop you can 'tweak' your day in order to eat at more socially accept-able times.

When I was first learning to listen to my hunger and sat-isfaction signals I always waited until my stomach told me I was hungry and ate until I truly was satisfied. Initially this meant that I would go without food for anything up to eight hours during the day and up to 16 hours overnight. I found a pattern emerging whereby I would eat breakfast and an evening meal one day and then the next day would only need lunch, with possibly just an apple in the evening to tide me over until breakfast. I did not snack at all in between and I also avoided sugary drinks as I knew this could numb my sensitivity. By doing this I was effectively halving my previous food consumption but because I knew that I was free to eat anything at any time I needed to I did-n't feel at all deprived.

But once I understood better how my own body operated I decided that I would prefer to eat less food but more often, and so be able to sit down and eat at least a main meal with my family. My own lifestyle led me to want to have this main meal in the early evening, sometime around 6pm. This not only fits in with the rest of the family but also leaves me with the evenings free to do other things. I know that if I eat too much at lunchtime my body isn't usually ready for this, so even if I am quite hungry in the middle of the day I still, now, won't eat to my 'satisfaction' point. Pro-viding that I don't eat too late at night I am usually ready to eat some breakfast, but again I don't generally eat much. My day's eating typically looks like this. . .

Breakfast	Hunger level	0 to ¼	Eat to ¾ point
Lunch	Hunger level	0 to ¼	Eat to ½ point
Evening	Hunger level	0 to ¼	Eat to S point

By following this plan I am able to eat at socially recognised times without overeating. If I have eaten later at night or have reached a definite full point at this meal, then I may well not bother with breakfast at all and my plan adapts something like this. . .

Breakfast	Hunger level	¼ to ½	Eat nothing
Mid-morning	Hunger level	0	Eat to ¾ point
Evening	Hunger level	0 to ¼	Eat to S

If, as often happens on Sunday, I wish to have the main family meal at lunchtime, I again have to adapt my eating accordingly. This time my day looks something like this. . .

Breakfast	Hunger level	0	Eat to ½ maximum
	Hunger level	¼ to ½	Eat nothing
Lunch	Hunger level	0	Eat to S
Evening	Hunger level	½ to ¾	Don't eat at all
	Hunger level	0 to ¼	Eat to ½ maximum

You will note, from the above examples, that I still never start to eat if I am more than a quarter full and that the 'tweaking' comes at the other end of the scale, by not eating as much as I could, given my physiological state. It is important to do this rather than thinking that you will eat just a little when already half to three-quarters full, as you will be too easily tempted to go beyond the satisfaction mark and thus put weight on.

When I was sticking strictly to eating only when I was truly empty, and having sufficient to fill me every time, it was a relatively easy (albeit antisocial) routine to follow. Once I started to adapt my responses as illustrated above, I had to be far more disciplined and conscious of what my stomach felt like when it was half or three-quarters full, so as not to be too full when the time came to eat with my family. This didn't happen straight away. I had a tendency to eat more than I planned and then not be ready for the main meal, but by trial and error I soon began to get where I wanted, and I am confident that, with the Lord's help and a little practice, the same will happen for you.

All the time I was reducing my weight I still ate only the equivalent of three full meals over two days – a far cry from the 'three square meals a day' regime which suited our ancestors. But I should add that at this time I didn't have a very energetic lifestyle. My work involved a lot of sitting at a word processor, driving and sitting in meetings! Now that I have reached the weight that is right for me and have a greater commitment to doing more exercise, my hunger levels and food consumption have altered accordingly. Our aim is not to eat a specified number of calories, as with a pre-scribed diet, but to eat what we need at any given time. Once you get used to this new way of managing your food intake you will find it liberating. You really can trust your body to 'speak' to you, especially when you remember that the Holy Spirit indwells you and that you have made a quality deci-sion to let Him take control. This is walking by faith, not by sight. It is not only far more effective, but exciting, and through this very practical application of scriptural truths you will learn to walk by faith in other areas of your life also.

If you have a medical condition which governs when you should eat, you will need to make allowances for that. For instance, if you are required to take medication first thing in the morning, with or after food, then you will need to eat something, regardless of your hunger level, but it needn't be much. If you have to eat at regular times of the day because of diabetes or some other condition, then you can seek to stop short of your satisfaction levels in order not to over-indulge, and always have some emergency snack with you, just in case. Fit For Life Forever advocates a walk of faith, but it is also one of common sense. Don't do anything foolish.

Practical Advice

In conclusion to this chapter, I wish to leave you with some practical suggestions which I trust will help you apply the principle of listening to your body's hunger and satisfaction signals to your own life. Read them, try them out, and use what works for you.

1. Pray before you eat. If you are already a committed Christian you probably give thanks to God every time you sit down to eat a meal. Why not simply extend what you already do by asking God to help you regulate your eating so that you do not abuse your body by eating too much.

2. Eat slowly. Not only does eating fast diminish the emotional satisfaction of eating and make it more difficult to receive accurate signals from your brain telling you you've had enough, it also leaves you staring at your empty plate while others are still eating. This, for those of us who are tempted to overeat, is risky, because we don't like to watch others eat without joining in. So what do we do? We look round to see if there are any seconds and eat extra just to keep ourselves occupied. I still have to make a conscious effort not to eat too fast but here are a couple of strategies that really help me. First, I try to put my fork down in between bites – this way I don't have food continually waiting to pop into my mouth; and, when I am eating with others, I try to engage in *either* conversation *or* eating, not both!

3. *Eat the best bits first.* Many people prefer to leave the best bits of their meal until last, so that they always have something to look forward to. However, when following the *Fit For Life Forever* principles this isn't necessarily the wisest move. The last thing you want is to reach your point of satisfaction and then have to say no to the best part of the meal! A better ploy would be to eat the best bits first, then you won't find it so difficult to leave what you don't need – that's as long as your best bits aren't the french fries!

4. *Don't expect to eat a lot.* You will be surprised, when you get into this way of eating, how little food it takes to fully satisfy you. And when you know that you can eat again whenever you feel hungry, you won't feel deprived like you have done on conventional diets. One emotion that I did have to wrestle with in the early stages, however, was a sense of loss. When I sat with others who seemed to tuck in with impunity, I remembered how I used to match the best of them. I even have a Hungryman Certificate as proof that I managed to finish an enormous plate of food, which qualified me for a free dessert! (Do you see that 'value for

money' mentality at work again?) So I experienced some-thing akin to grief, realising that I would not be joining them any more. When it comes to food, we envy those who seem to need a lot to keep them going, don't we? But then I found a new way of looking at it . . . If I had a car that gave me more miles to the gallon than others, I would count myself fortunate to have a motor that worked so economi-cally. Well, our bodies operate on the same principle as cars – fuel in, energy out. Now, if I appear to have less on my plate than others, I thank God for giving me a fuel-efficient engine! Again in the early days, when I didn't yet know how to regulate my portions, I would eat too much for my main course and then not have room for dessert. Now, if I want to eat dessert, I know to give myself a smaller portion for a main course. Sometimes it doesn't look much, but it's usually ample now that my stomach has reduced to its healthy size.

5. *Use a smaller plate.* This will psychologically help you to cope with having smaller portions. A small plate which appears full will not leave you feeling cheated, whereas a large dinner plate with only a small portion might. When you have eaten enough remove the plate straight away so that you will not be tempted to pick.

6. *Remove serving dishes from the table.* All the time that you have food in serving dishes staring you in the face you will be more tempted to replenish your plate. Once you have served the meal, put the serving dishes or pans out of sight. If, once your plate is empty, you genuinely are still hungry, you can, of course, get some more, but start with less than

you would normally serve and you may be surprised to find that it really is enough to satisfy you.

7. *Demarcate your personal eating space* by using a place mat. When you do this you may be less tempted to look outside of your parameters for more food.

8. *When in doubt wait and pray.* Before you automatically sit down to eat, ask yourself, 'Am I ready to eat yet? Am I really hungry?' If you don't know, then you're almost certainly not! If possible wait another half hour, and then reassess your hunger levels. While you are eating, continue to wait and pray at intervals to discern whether or not you have eaten sufficient to make you satisfied. Remember, you can always eat some more if you are still hungry, but if you eat more than you need, there's no going back.

9. *Reject unhelpful or negative thoughts and beliefs.* Review some of the false and unhelpful beliefs we unearthed in Chapter 6. Try to become aware of how these are working against listening to your body's hunger and satisfaction signals. God's word exhorts us to bring our thoughts captive and bring them into obedience to Christ. When you find yourself thinking false or negative thoughts, replace them with the truth of Scripture. Remember, what a person believes rules him or her. In point 4 above, I wrote of the negative feelings of loss and resentment I felt because I didn't need as much food as I used to eat, but I replaced these with positive thoughts which enabled me to see myself, not as deprived, but as fortunate. If you cultivate this way of looking at things, with the help and inspiration of the Holy Spirit you, too, will be an overcomer.

I hope that you are beginning to see that listening for your body's hunger and satisfaction signals not only makes sound sense, but is also manageable whatever your individual lifestyle. The more that you include God in the equation and the more submitted you are to the lordship of Christ in your life, so the greater your personal bodily awareness will become. After all, He created you and He dwells within all those who have put their trust in Him. This is a walk by faith, not by sight, where you are learning to let the Holy Spirit be your guide. You have probably already learnt to trust Him in other areas of your life, so dare to trust Him in this most practical and personal area also. Will you get it right immediately? Probably not! Because, like everything else, learning to listen is a process. You are on a learning curve, but as you seek daily to practise these two principles you will go from faith to faith, you will discern your own body more accurately and you will be free forever from a dependency on external rules and regulations.

Home Assignments

1. Over the next three days, complete the Hunger and Satisfaction Log in Appendix 4. The aim of this is to help you regulate your eating so that you start to eat as close to empty as possible and end no fuller than satisfied.
2. Try and describe what true hunger feels like to you.
3. How often in the past have you waited until you were truly hungry before eating? Be honest!
4. Look at the practical advice to help you eat within your hunger and satisfaction levels. Introduce one thing at a time, in any order you prefer, until you are doing all you can to help regulate your eating.

13

Freedom to Choose

Having read an overview of the principles of this book and the Fit For Life Forever course, you have already been introduced to this radical idea that you are free to choose whatever foods you want. Whoever heard of that as a way to lose weight? And yet I, and many, many others, are living proof that it works. In this chapter you are going to learn how to eat in total freedom and at the same time shed those extra pounds – permanently!

The first thing we need to consider is the spiritual principle that God wants us to live in freedom, to be healthy, to look our best and to succeed in our weight management goals. Please notice that there are four parts to this confession: living in freedom, being healthy, looking good, and succeeding in managing our weight. We cannot just take the first point, 'living in freedom', in isolation, otherwise our freedom may well become licence and we will not be healthy, nor look good, nor succeed in our weight management goals. Those of us acquainted with some of the fundamental spiritual principles of the Christian life know that, in Christ, freedom does not imply irresponsibility or licence.

It does not mean that we throw caution to the wind and live without any personal restraint. But what it does mean is that we have been liberated from the curse of the law, free now to live a life of grace, through faith, by the power of the Holy Spirit. These truths not only apply to the changing of our inner nature into the likeness of Christ, but to the most fundamental aspects of our daily life, including how and what we eat.

One of the most exciting discoveries I have ever made regarding having a Spirit-controlled appetite, has been this realisation that I am no longer under the law, but under grace – grace, in this sense, being the divine ability to fulfil God's commands. Whenever I had tried to lose weight in the conventional sense of 'going on a diet' I had always prayed that God would help me to succeed. As I braced myself for another round of calorie counting and dietary restrictions I would ask God for the strength to stick to the plan and not to give in to temptation. To give God His due, I believe that He did strengthen me and, generally speaking (providing my resolve was strong enough), I did shed the pounds and did give Him the glory. But my success was always short lived and eventually the weight crept back on and usually left me heavier than before the diet began. Needless to say I would feel very condemned by this, reasoning that I had failed not only my diet, but the Lord Himself.

But following my experience of weight gain when we returned from Tanzania, as I once again faced my urgent need to lose weight, I felt a distinct prompting *not* to go on a diet, and so I began to pray that the Lord would show me personally what I needed to do to achieve permanent results. As I, on the one hand, prayed that He would show me when and what to eat, I began to see an amusing parallel between what I had hitherto tried to do and the folly of the 'new creation' trying to adhere to the intricacies of the Old Testament Law. This came to me through the following Scripture:

> Let no one judge you in food or drink . . . why . . . do you subject yourself to regulations – "Do not touch, do not taste, do not handle". . . . These things indeed have an appearance of wisdom in self-imposed religion, false humility, and neglect of the body, but are of no value against the indulgence of the flesh. (Colossians 2:16, 20–23, NKJV)

I appreciate that this passage in Colossians relates contextually to a situation in which some teachers were advocating the legalism of circumcision and observance of Hebrew laws and traditions in order to please God. It has nothing, literally, to do with diets! Nevertheless I believe that these warnings against legalism, when viewed alongside other scriptures, are in the general spirit of what Christ purposes to do in our lives. When I read these words it was as though the Lord was saying to me, 'Why do you keep asking Me to help you stick to a diet? You might just as well have asked Me to help you keep all the requirements of the Levitical Law!' Of course, as a born-again Christian I understood that for those of us who are 'in Christ' such demands are obsolete, Christ having been, for us, a fulfilment of the Law. To follow a diet regime is not morally wrong, but there is a more excellent way.

This passage in Colossians draws attention to the effects of trying to keep these laws on our lives. Firstly it has 'an appearance of wisdom'. Since all diet regimes seek, in some way, to cut down our calorie consumption, and some also seek to make us eat more healthily, this is certainly true. From a mechanistic point of view it has to work, but the problem is we are not machines! We do not function purely on the physical level of 'calories in = energy out' and to try to make us operate on this mathematical plane denies our humanity. An *appearance* of wisdom – certainly, but true wisdom – No! Why? Because for 98% of us it simply doesn't work.

Next, the passage speaks of self-imposed religion. Many definitions of religion include the idea of a strict adherence to a set of rules. Now, doesn't that sound somewhat akin to going on a diet? And how about, 'Do not touch, do not taste, do not handle'? I had been subjecting myself to these kinds of regulations every time I had followed a diet regime, and all that they ever did was to make me long for the forbidden foods more and more!

How about the 'false humility'? I hope you do not think I am stretching the point here, but whenever I hear people speak about their diet experiences they refer to having been 'good' or 'bad' depending on whether they measured up to the requirements. When they admit to being 'naughty' for eating a piece of chocolate or french fries it is, on face value, like a confession of sin; but while there may be regret that they have not been as self-disciplined as they hoped, this falls far short of genuine repentance. However, since the 'sin' isn't actually real – the failed standard having been self-imposed, not initiating from God – neither can 'repentance' and its associated humility be of any intrinsic value either.

The verse goes on to speak about the 'neglect of the body'. Surely, diets are all about *looking after* our bodies?

Well, in principle, yes – this may be so, but I hope I have explained well enough in the chapter entitled 'Diets Don't Work', for you to see that as well as being ineffective in producing permanent weight loss, many diets, especially those with severe calorie restrictions, actually harm the body by slowing down metabolism, depriving it of essential nutrients and destroying muscle tissue.

But the greatest eye-opener provided by this verse of Scripture is the final phrase which reads: 'but are of no value against the indulgence of the flesh.' How true this is of a conventional diet! Like the Pharisees of old, the best that we can attain to with our diet is to 'clean the outside of the cup' (Matthew 23:25). Our shape may temporarily change for the better, but our success is purely cosmetic. The inner roots to our disordered eating have not been addressed at all! It is like the lazy gardener who instead of digging up the dandelion roots simply removes the foliage. In no time at all the weeds shoot up again, stronger than ever before. Just as the Old Testament Law could not tame the passions of the flesh, no more can a diet tame the passions of our runaway appetites. The law of diets may be logical and good regarding the mathematics of energy in and energy out, but there is '. . . another law in my members, warring against the law of my mind, and bringing me into captivity to the law of sin. . . ' (Romans 7:23, NKJV), which is evidenced as passions and lusts, including lust for food. Just like the apostle Paul, many of us facing up to our inability to stick to a diet might declare, 'the good that I will to do, I do not do, but the evil I will not to do, that I practice!' (Romans 7:19, NKJV).

And who can deliver us from this curse? The same One

who delivers us from all our temptations – Christ Himself! He does this not by threats, neither merely by strengthening our resolve to do better. He does this through 'the immeasurable greatness of His power toward us who believe' (Ephesians 1:19). As we reckon ourselves to be dead to the old nature, crucified with Christ, and submit ourselves to God, so the seed of the new nature begins to grow within us and we are changed from one degree of glory into another by the Spirit of God. What God works within our lives with respect to our disordered eating is exactly the same as He does with respect to any other aspect of our fallen nature – He puts the old to death and brings forth the new creation, made in the image of Christ. We find as we walk in the Spirit that we no longer fulfil the lusts of the flesh. Our appetite is under the control of the Spirit of God and we no longer abuse our bodies by feeding them wrongly, either by excess or by what is harmful.

One aspect of the fruit of the Spirit, as described in Galatians 5:22–23, is 'self-control'. For many years I understood this to be, by definition, control *by* the self. This is the only way that the world can define it. It is akin to 'pulling our socks up', strengthening our resolve, or being more determined. But think about it . . . Can I effectively call upon the resources of my self-nature to help me overcome the deficiencies which lie within it? Of course not! It is like calling upon Satan to cast out Satan – an impossibility! That is why you have never been able to draw upon your self-control to curb your appetite. But when the Bible talks about self-control, there is a subtle yet far-reaching difference. It is not control *by* the self, but control *of* the self. The controller is the Holy Spirit, not me, and this makes the world of difference. As we yield to His control, knowing that without Him we can do nothing, then He does the work and the fruit which we see in our own lives truly does give glory to our Heavenly Father.

In Romans 7:6 we read: '. . . now we are released from the law, having died to that which held us captive, so that we serve not under the old written code but in the new life of the Spirit.' Again, I should be clear in stating that the law, as referred to in Scripture, has nothing to do theologically with any secular legal system or rules. Nevertheless it is a valid observation and a real encouragement to realise that we no longer have to operate under the old written code of diet regimes but can, even in this respect, live instead the life of the Spirit, which is one of total freedom and victory as we yield our lives to God.

God is Not a Killjoy!

The ascetic, self-denying lifestyle of a religious order may be well intentioned, but it is not the way for most of us, and is powerless against the demands of our flesh nature. God did not allow the creation of desserts and delicious savouries just to test us! We read in His word that 'everything created by God is good, and nothing is to be rejected if it is received with thanksgiving' (1 Timothy 4:4). Again in 1 Timothy 6:17 we read that 'God . . . richly provides us with everything to enjoy'. When God put Adam and Eve in the Garden of Eden there was only one restriction – the fruit of the Tree of Knowledge of Good and Evil. Concerning the rest He said: 'You may surely eat. . . ' (Genesis 2:16).

Within this general framework, Scripture does allow for

individual conscience and exhorts us to make allowances for this with each other.

> One person believes he may eat anything, while the weak person eats only vegetables. Let not the one who eats despise the one who abstains, and let not the one who abstains pass judgment on the one who eats, for God has welcomed him. Who are you to pass judgment on the servant of another? It is before his own master that he stands or falls. (Romans 14: 2–4a)

For those like me, whose conscience allows the consumption of all foods, the injunction is not to despise, or mock, or show disrespect for those who choose to follow certain restrictions regarding their food. For others who believe that certain foods ought not to be consumed, they are not to judge those of us who exercise a greater freedom. 'Whatever does not proceed from faith is sin' we read in Romans 14:23, and this puts personal responsibility on each one of us to follow our own conscience in these matters. We shall see later in this chapter that wisdom may decree that you decide before God not to touch certain foods, for a period of time at least, and in such cases you, as an individual, should follow the leading of the Holy Spirit. This is not bringing yourself into the bondage of food laws, but being obedient to the Lord in respect of your own life and situation.

The Devil's Half-truths

The Bible describes the devil as the 'Father of Lies' (John 8:44), but we all know that it is often easier to deceive with a half-truth than it is with an outright and obvious lie. This cunning of Satan is first recorded in the third chapter of

Genesis where he successfully tempts Eve to eat of the forbidden fruit. It may or may not be significant, but I find it interesting at least that the first recorded temptation in the Bible was to do with food! In verse 1 Satan, in the form of a serpent, says: 'Did God actually say, "You shall not eat of *every* tree of the garden?"' – implying, through this half-truth, that God was overly restrictive in His demands. Eve is alert enough to correct Satan and replies (verse 2): 'We may eat of the fruit of the trees in the garden, but God said, "You shall not eat of the fruit of the tree that is in the midst of the garden, neither shall you *touch it,* lest you die."' This is another half-truth, for God had said nothing at all about not touching the fruit. Finally the devil speaks an outright lie: 'You will not surely die,' which is a direct contradiction of what God had actually spoken in 2:17.

In our enlightened day and age, much research is taking place into every aspect of food, health and eating – so much so that it is quite difficult to keep abreast of the findings. Every day, or so it seems, there is some new report being aired through the media telling us of the dangers of eating this, that or the other. And several times I have seen people throw up their hands in despair, asking, 'Isn't there anything safe to eat?' To add to this, many reports are contradictory and (in order to be fair to the reader) I have already quoted from some of these in the last chapter. Are we confused? You bet your life we are!

But this, too, is the devil's ploy. He is the author of confusion, and if he can spread his gospel of fear and deprivation through well-qualified experts, so much the better so far as he is concerned. I do not wish to be flippant regarding these things, neither to disregard well-documented and widely held health warnings, but I want you to consider for a moment certain statements which we have come to accept as 'gospel'. Read, if you will, the following three statements concerning food and eating, and ask yourself whether, as regards your own beliefs, these statements are true:

1. Some foods are good while others are bad.
2. Some foods will give you cancer, heart attacks, stroke, diabetes, etc.
3. You should never eat foods which are high in sugar, fat, salt, etc.

Well, how did you answer? Many of you, I imagine, will have replied yes to all three of these statements. But I propose to you that, as they stand, none of these statements is completely true. Rather they are *half*-truths and that makes them less than helpful when it comes to regulating our weight. So let us examine them more closely.

The first is, 'Some foods are good while others are bad.' If we take this statement at face value, then we are in fact ascribing to food the moral qualities of 'goodness' and 'badness'. Of course, you are intelligent enough to know that this isn't the case, and you probably instinctively added the words 'for you to eat' to the statement, even if only in your subconscious. But the problem of consenting to the half-truth is that, subconsciously, it can produce within us a moral response when we eat foods which we perceive as being forbidden. It is but a short leap in our profession to go from saying, 'this food is bad' to believing 'I was bad for eating it'. When this happens we believe that we have somehow sinned or at least let ourselves down. This makes us feel a failure, lowers our self-esteem and makes it harder than ever to achieve our weight goals. What would be truthful, and what is really meant by the statement, is that some foods are *more nutritious* than others. No one can argue with this, and faced with the fact of the matter we are free to make up our own mind regarding whether or not to partake.

The second statement reads: 'Some foods will give you cancer, heart attacks, stroke, diabetes, etc.' But is this decisively true? Again, the answer is 'no', because it neither takes into account the amount or frequency of consumption, nor the effect of different foods on us as individuals. What would be true would be to say that some foods, *taken to excess*, are likely *to increase the probability* of developing these various illnesses.

And what about the third statement, that we 'should never eat foods which are high in sugar, fat, salt, etc.'? Is this true? Well, we would certainly be unwise not to heed the health warnings associated with the proven links between excessive salt intake and high blood pressure, or those between high cholesterol and heart disease or high-calorie foods and obesity. But our bodies *do* need some salt, they *do* need some fats, and the occasional high-calorie, low-nutrient food will not do any harm in an otherwise healthy body. Again, the true statement needs to include words pertaining to excess. Also, replacing the prohibitive, paternalistic words, 'You should never' with the words, 'It would be wise not to' are less likely to produce within us a negative, rebellious, self-destructive, response. Now our statement reads: 'It would be wise to limit your intake of foods which have an excessive amount of sugar, salt or unhealthy fats.' I can say, 'Amen to that!'

Perhaps you think that I am arguing unnecessarily over

semantics – simply playing with words, but I think not. For what happens when we hold to these various half-truths, without proper qualification, is that we respond in negative ways, becoming fearful about eating all manner of food and filled with guilt when we do.

One likely response is that we become *obsessive* over what to eat. We analyse everything in minute detail. When we go out to eat (or in other ways are not in control of the ingredients) we wonder what hidden dangers are lurking beneath the attractive, alluring façade. We can never take food on face value and the enjoyment of eating is lost for us. We stick to what we consider to be 'safe' foods, but these so often seem bland and unimaginative. Although our stomachs are filled we remain *emotionally unsatisfied.*

If we wish to totally avoid these hidden dangers then we must omit many foods from our diet altogether. This is a costly price to pay and we may feel that to remain healthy we must *deprive ourselves* totally of the foods we have hitherto enjoyed. I do not believe that such a heavy burden comes from the Lord.

I am very wary when it comes to processed pre-packaged foods, especially cheaper brands with artificial flavours, artificial colourings, and loaded with empty starch calories and chemicals to add bulk and to make them palatable. God did not create these, man did, and they are a poor substitute for the real thing. Felicity Lawrence, consumer affairs correspondent for *The Guardian* expresses her contempt for processed food like this:

> The fresh foods which provide vital nutrients, the vitamins, minerals and essential fatty acids we need for health, are being

replaced by large quantities of hardened fats, sugars and salt. . . We are being fed junk and it is making us sick.[1]

Let us not tempt God by deliberately eating harmful produce, but neither let us be fearful. If we cannot afford organic food, or it is not readily available, we can trust God that as long as we do what we can regarding food hygiene, He will look after us. I have worked as a missionary for several years and have had some food put before me which I would never eat at home and which has been prepared under the most unsavoury conditions. God gives the necessary grace to eat it and, as I give thanks, I believe that His hand of protection is upon me. Very rarely have I experienced any stomach upset.

Eating in Freedom

How do we eat in freedom? I want us to examine two overlapping scriptures, both of which, contextually, have to do with food (though again it ought to be said they are *not* talking about diet regimes). They are both found in 1 Corinthians. The first is in 1 Corinthians 6:12, and the second in 10:23. Both begin by saying: 'All things are lawful.' What does this word 'lawful' mean? To gain more of an understanding, here is a list of meanings as taken from the composite verses in the Amplified Bible: '. . . allowable, legitimate, permissible, you are free to do anything you please.' Are there any exceptions to this injunction? No, there are none, because the scripture clearly says '*All* things.' Wow!

---

[1] Lawrence, Felicity, *Not on the Label* (Penguin, 2004)

This means that, *in principle,* you can have that doughnut, or those french fries, or some chocolate or full-fat cheese. You don't have to stick to celery sticks, low-fat or vegetarian cheese, cream crackers without spread or even low-fat milk. You can eat all your favourite foods and you can eat in total freedom. In fact, you might like to pause right here and make out a list of your ten most favourite foods. Go right ahead and include those chocolates or banoffee pie! Now read it out loud and thank God for His permission to eat those foods. You are taking a step of faith!

Our fallen human nature will always gravitate towards what is forbidden. We will always want what we think we can't have. But God hasn't placed such heavy rules regarding food upon us; well-meaning dieticians have! Let us remind ourselves that we are not under the law any more, we are under grace. 'For freedom Christ has set us free; stand firm therefore, and do not submit again to a yoke of slavery' (Galatians 5:1).

Eating Responsibly

A. W. Tozer, a much-acclaimed American Bible teacher of the twentieth century, has said that 'Truth is like a bird; it cannot fly on one wing.' We should consider, therefore, not only 'It is written' but 'It is also written'.[2] So what I have presented so far, although it is, I believe, the truth, is only one wing. Left on its own our bird is going to fall to the ground and perish! The other 'wing', so to speak, is found

---

[2] Tozer, A. W., *That Incredible Christian* (Camp Hill, PA: Christian Publications, 1964)

in the other half of those verses in 1 Corinthians that I have already quoted. So, at this point, let us look at what these verses say, quoted in full:

1 Corinthians 6:12, 13a: 'All things are lawful for me, but all things are not helpful. All things are lawful for me but I will not be brought under the power of any. Food for the stomach and the stomach for foods' (NKJV).

1 Corinthians 10:23 reads: 'All things are lawful for me, but not all things are helpful; all things are lawful for me, but not all things edify' (NKJV).

Again, using the composite verse from the Amplified Bible, these verses include the following ideas . . . not everything is helpful, good for me to do, expedient, profitable and wholesome, and conclude with this thought: 'when considered with other things.'

This means that although I have the freedom to eat doughnuts, it may not be helpful when considered against my need to remain healthy; it means that although I am allowed to eat potato crisps, it may not be good for me to do considered against my hopes of losing weight; it is legitimate for me to eat full-fat ice-cream with caramel topping and fresh cream, but it may not be expedient if I want to fit into smaller jeans. Can you see the balance? Along with the freedom is a corresponding obligation to eat *responsibly*.

I do hope this explanation hasn't left you feeling disappointed. Perhaps, now that these verses have been explained more fully, you are thinking that what is *theoretically* acceptable, in practice is not, that your hopes have been raised only to be dashed again. If this is so, take heart, for this is definitely not the case. Since starting on this road of freedom with responsibility, I have, from time to time, eaten all of these high-calorie foods mentioned above, and have done so without a hint of guilt and with a steady loss of weight. But what I have found is that, as I have submitted my appetite to God on a daily basis, my desire for certain high-calorie, low-nutrient foods has diminished. Today I will often choose a portion of fruit in preference to a piece of cake, or a salad instead of french fries, and when I do eat fries – maybe, on average, once a week – I need less than a dozen on my plate to be satisfied.

I have also done a lot of my own research, and completed a course on nutrition. I pray about what I am reading and make my own judgements. For instance, I used to eat a lot of sausage and beefburger, but then as I understood just what ingredients were allowed under the general heading of 'meat' I became suspicious! Apparently, by EU law,[3] 'meat' can include up to 25% fat and 25% skin; sinew and gristle are also permitted (so your '100% meat beefburger' doesn't have to contain much muscle at all!). I now much prefer to eat meals which I can prepare from scratch and, if I do occasionally choose convenience foods, I read very carefully the nutritional information on the labels before I buy.

Although I most certainly eat more healthily than I once did, I do not always go for the low-fat, low-sugar or low carbohydrate options. For one thing, I have discovered that where a manufacturer takes pains to reduce the levels of

---

[3] 'Meat Products Labelling', EU Commission Directive (2002/86/EC)

one element and promotes its health values accordingly, the levels of other ingredients are often increased to make the food more palatable! In other words: less fat = more sugar, or less sugar = more fat. It really is swings and roundabouts at the end of the day.

I have found, for myself, that the taste and texture of some low-fat foods is very unsatisfying. Take low-fat cheese, for instance. When I was trying it out, I realised that I was consuming large amounts to make up for the relative lack of taste and that a smaller portion of a conventional cheese, with lots of taste, amounted to less calories in the end and satisfied me more. This is a purely personal thing, and you will need to find out what suits you.

The important thing is to be sensible and accountable. I have had regular health checks to measure my sugar levels and cholesterol and, since these are all well within the acceptable bounds, I do not feel that I need to make unnecessary sacrifices here. I usually eat butter, for instance, instead of a low-fat spread, but I use it sparingly. If, however, my cholesterol was found to be high and / or there was a genetic disposition towards heart disease, then I would really pray about cutting butter out and eating less red meat. I have also found that I just don't desire anywhere near the same amounts of refined carbohydrates that I once consumed, and my natural choice is for lower-glycaemic foods such as granary bread, whole grains and pulses.

Now I do happen to have a genetic predisposition towards high blood pressure, so although it is below the danger level since losing weight, I do not tempt providence by overdoing the salt. Tastebuds very quickly adapt to changes in diet and I have now found that I need far less salt than previously. So, if there is a low-salt option I will usually choose it, partly out of health considerations, but more so now because I prefer the taste.

If you have your own blood pressure, cholesterol and sugar levels checked, and all is well; then there is no reason why you cannot eat just what you want, *within reason,* in accordance with your hunger and satisfaction levels. In view of what is known about the links between high GI foods and their cumulative effect on sugar levels and insulin resistance, it would be wise to monitor your intake of carbohydrates, choosing for regular consumption those foods with a lower GI. If your cholesterol is high, you will want to lower your intake of saturated and hydrogenated (hardened) fats, and if your blood pressure is high, you might seriously consider lowering your salt intake. (Please note, however, that most of our salt consumption does not come from what we add to food in cooking or at the table, but that 75% of our consumption is 'hidden' in manufactured food, to help preserve it and to mask the unpleasant taste of chemical additives.)

The main thing to take into account, generally speaking, is how much you are consuming overall. It is the excesses that cause the problems; the excesses that pile on the weight; the excesses that make us lethargic and adversely affect our health. Learn to eat primarily for physiological reasons, to satisfy your hunger and then (providing there are no other incidental health issues) you can partake of all the rich variety of food God has provided for our enjoyment – in moderation. If you already have a diagnosed medical condition (as we have discussed before) then you will need to make the necessary adjustments to your diet, but where this is the case, God will give the necessary grace. Of course, He is able to heal you completely, so believe for the best, but do not go against your doctor's advice unless you have a very clear personal word from the Lord; otherwise you will be walking in presumption, not faith.

Making Personal Choices

As you seek to take responsibility for your personal 'diet' – by which I mean the kinds of food you choose to eat, not a prescribed regime – I want you to appreciate that there is no one right way to eat. As we have said before, we are all individuals and what suits one will not necessarily suit the other. Understand also that you are on a learning curve and that your choices will change and develop: firstly, as you understand the needs of your own body, secondly as you learn more about nutrition, and thirdly as you become more confident in handling your freedom in Christ. To help you make these personal choices, here are a few guidelines:

1. Pray about what you should eat and be obedient to what God shows you. Remember that God created you and knows you intimately. He knows your optimum weight and your pre-designed shape and He also knows exactly what you need to eat both to fulfil the nutritional needs of your body and to satisfy your personal taste. In view of all this, it makes good sense, prior to anything else, to pray. As well as asking the Lord to help us not to eat beyond our satisfaction point we could also ask Him to help us to make wise, yet palatable, choices.

A good time to do this is when we go to the supermarket.

If you make a shopping list (and I believe this is a good practice as it helps avoid impulse purchasing), then ask the Lord to guide you as you draw it up. If you find yourself wanting to include foods that you love, even though they happen to be high-calorie or low-nutrient, then simply check it out with the Lord, and if you have peace, go right ahead and buy it. If you don't have peace, then be obedient to the inner prompting and leave it out.

Remember that you are learning to walk by faith. But faith will grow even as you grow. If you have a personal history which demonstrates a real weakness with respect to certain foods (chocolate, for instance) and you know that in the past it has been fatal to have such food in the house, then you may feel, before God, that it would be wise for you not to be exposed to this temptation. When we individually introduce certain rules into our life to help us live accountably, this is not legalism; when we seek to inflict our own rules onto others, that is. According to the Word of God, we go 'from faith to faith' (Romans 1:17, NKJV), so to try and live beyond our present level of faith is to court disaster. While you might reasonably expect to experience setbacks from time to time, you don't want to deliberately increase this probability by taking steps which leave you anxious. It is said of wisdom that 'all her paths are peace' (Proverbs 3:17), so if you don't have peace, don't do it!

Outside of home shopping, the main time when we need to make food choices occurs when we are eating in a restaurant. Once again it is good to pray, showing a willingness to be guided by the Holy Spirit. When I was trying to lose weight through a diet regime, there was nothing worse than going out for a meal on a special occasion and then spoiling it for myself by not daring to eat what I really, really wanted because it was high in calories. Listen, it isn't what we occasionally eat that causes us to put weight on but the steady abuse of our bodies on a day-to-day basis. I came across this little saying some time back and I think it is worth pondering: 'It isn't what you eat between Christmas and the New Year that will damage you, but what you eat between the New Year and Christmas!' Now I am not advocating that we all throw caution to the wind and go on an unrestrained binge, even at Christmas, but within reason, and certainly on special treats, choose what you really, really want. I find food portions served in restaurants to be generally far more than I need so, rather than restrict my choice of food, I am far more likely to leave some on my plate or not order a dessert. You might also see if someone would like to share with you, giving you the opportunity to enjoy smaller quantities but with a wider selection.

2. Eat only the foods that you enjoy. Whenever you have sought to lose weight by following some conventional or fad diet you have probably had to get used to eating bland foods that didn't really satisfy you. Or perhaps you were allowed to eat all kinds of food, but you had to avoid certain combinations. So you could have roast beef, say, but would have to leave your Yorkshire pudding and roast potatoes for another meal, or you could have curry as long as it wasn't with rice or naan bread. What possible satisfaction can be found in that, I wonder? You can keep this up for a while, maybe, but it is life habits that we want to develop if weight loss is to be maintained. The bottom line is this: if you are not enjoying the food that you are eating you will not be able to keep it up. Before long, your feelings of deprivation will get the better of you and you will go out and binge on the very foods that you have been told to avoid.

I was at my hairdresser's the other day and she told me that she was once again on a diet. She was quite pleased with her progress, she said, but before long I heard her remark that she was 'starving'. She momentarily slipped out of the salon and re-emerged holding a dry cream cracker. She munched her way through this and then went out for another. 'Are you enjoying them?' I enquired. I don't think she had even considered this before, it seemed irrelevant! After considering my question a moment, she gave her reply: 'Not especially,' she told me, 'but they only have a few calories so I can eat as many as I want.' This is bondage!

Perhaps you do not really know which foods you enjoy. When I suggested earlier that you make a list of your ten favourite foods, did you find it easy or difficult? I find that many people on the Fit For Life Forever course have a problem initially with this. Let us explore why this may be so.

Some people have been dieting for so long and have abdicated their own food choices to the prescriptive rules of others that they are no longer in touch with their true preferences. In fact, the less conscious you are of your own desires, the easier it is to follow somebody else's plan. At least you feel safe, knowing that if you eat exactly what the diet tells you to eat, in the measured quantities it prescribes, then you won't overdo the calories and should, theoretically, lose weight.

Or maybe you have habitually cooked or eaten to fit in with the preferences of others. If you grew up in an atmosphere of overbearing control, then it may have been that

even in this matter of food, you never really had the freedom to choose what you personally wanted. You ate what
you were given and that was that. Then, if you married, you
just went along with what your partner enjoyed, not really
considering whether or not you might occasionally like to
eat something that wasn't on his or her list. (I am speaking
generically because, in this politically correct day and age,
there may well be men reading this who do the cooking for
their partner.) You may have even considered it to be selfish
to cook what *you* want. Even if you did initially know what
you liked, you may have decided as a matter of convenience to take the road of least resistance and comply with the
stronger preferences of your partner. In this way you learnt
to distance yourself from your own true desires.

Then there are others who seem to know exactly what
they would like to eat, but because the things that they
would like to eat are almost always the foods which have
hitherto been considered out of bounds, they have denied
their true desires in order to eat, out of obligation, only what
is classified as 'healthy'. Whenever they eat what they
really like they are filled with guilt, so they try to avoid eating them altogether. Then when the urge is overwhelming,
they binge on all the high-calorie, low-nutrient foods and
are filled with guilt. Perhaps this is you? The irony of all this
is that most of us, given the choice, *would* choose to eat
healthy food if we were not repeatedly told that other foods
were bad! This has certainly been true for me.

If you are one of those people having trouble knowing
what you really want to eat you could try the following
approach: (1) What flavour do I desire? (2) What temperature do I desire? (3) What texture do I want? (4) What

colour would I prefer? (Different coloured varieties of vegetables possess differing mineral properties, so eating a mix-
ture of red, green and yellow / white vegetables will give
you the balance your body needs.) These questions will
help you focus on your own particular preferences.

When you start to approach food choice in this specific
way, you may find yourself making some unusual decisions! I remember one lunchtime thinking to myself that I
really fancied some custard. The first obstacle I had to overcome was an old record playing in my mind that told me
that I couldn't have dessert because I *must* eat something
else first. It felt slightly 'naughty' just going for something
sweet on its own. Then, when I had given myself permission not to eat anything savoury, I still felt that it wasn't
quite 'kosher' to have custard on its own, so I began to look
around the kitchen to see what I could have with it. I found
both a treacle sponge pudding, and a Christmas pudding,
but I didn't fancy either. No, what I really wanted was a
bowl of thick, creamy, home-made custard, on its own!
Finally I decided to just do it. I made up about a third of a
pint (about 150 ml) of custard and enjoyed every mouthful.
When I had eaten it my appetite was satisfied; in fact
throughout the afternoon I kept thinking to myself how
good it had been! This is eating in liberty.

Since that day I have, on several occasions, chosen a
dessert for my midday meal. With my reduced food intake,
I often find when I eat my main meal (usually in the
evening) that I haven't really got room for a dessert and
that to have one then would take me past the 'satisfied'
point on my fuel gauge. Initially I would feel a bit cheated
about this, but then I reasoned that if in the past I had

repeatedly overeaten by consuming both in one meal, how much better to split it up and eat dessert at some other time of day, when I was really hungry? Theoretically this could be at breakfast, but for me this is still too much of a cultural shift! The important thing is to be free to follow your heart, without condemnation, and to find as a result that you are not only physically satisfied but emotionally satisfied as well.

Sometimes we find ourselves in situations where we are surrounded by all kinds of delicious food and we want to eat it all. This can happen at a buffet, which in times past was my Achilles' heel. I always overate at buffets because I wanted to make sure that I got good value for money. But when the Lord began to deal with this self-destructive, unhelpful way of thinking, and I stopped loading up my plate, I still needed a workable strategy so that I wouldn't feel cheated. I recognised that if I simply started at one end of the table, putting onto my plate everything that I enjoyed, my plate would already be full by the time I had reached halfway! I would resent it when I saw some other food on display which I would have preferred, but manners prevented me from returning the food I had already chosen! I have now solved this by taking the time, prior to putting anything on my plate, to walk along the line of food and prioritising in my mind which foods I would select. This means that I may not eat everything that I like, but at least I have chosen the ones I like best.

3. Do not use freedom as an excuse to indulge the flesh! Remember that freedom is not licence – either as regards food or anything else that we enjoy in Christ. This is plainly stated in Galatians 5:13, which reads: 'you were called to freedom, brothers. Only do not use your freedom as an opportunity for the flesh. . . ' Neither does our walk of grace give us an excuse to continue in irresponsibility and lust. Romans 6:1–2 and 15 read: 'What shall we say then? Shall we continue in sin that grace may abound?. . . Shall we sin because we are not under law but under grace?' The answer Paul gives us to both of these propositions is a resounding, 'Certainly not!' (NKJV).

Having been set free from diets, our safeguard against swinging too far to the other extreme lies in our submission to Christ. Some people feel a sense of repulsion at the mention of the word 'submission'. If this is the case with you, it may be due to having been subject, in your past history, to some form of spiritual abuse whereby you were ordered to 'submit' to an earthly, quasi-spiritual authority and did so out of guilt and fear. But submission is vastly different from subjection and, by definition, can never be forced upon anyone. Subjection is enforced by another from without and we have no choice in the matter, but to submit is to choose to yield as a free act of one's will. Where there is true love and trust, submission is never really an issue. The one who is submitting does so out of a heartfelt desire to yield up his or her rights to another, recognising that the one to whom submission is given would never abuse this in any way. In this case the One to whom we are submitting is none other than the Lord Jesus Christ, who has already demonstrated to us through His selfless life and sacrificial death that He is worthy of our surrender and trust. Even if, at times, His instruction to us cuts right across our own plans and desires, we know that His way is best and that He never withholds anything from us except that which He knows would harm us and prevent us from entering into His very best for our individual lives. (Please note, you are *not* being asked to submit your appetite to Fit For Life Forever, or any earthly authority.)

Only when we have truly yielded to God can we fully taste and enjoy the freedom Christ has purchased on our behalf. If we know, deep down, that we are reserving some areas of our lives for our self-nature to live on unjudged and uncrucified, then we cannot hope to exercise true discernment even in the matter of food choice. Instead we will rationalise and make excuses and hide from our true, fallen nature. But once we have come to this place of surrender, then from thereon in our path – even if it appears to others to be narrow – is in reality as broad as heaven itself.

Sometimes the Lord will test our submission. But such testing is never to let Him know the response of our hearts, for He knows this already. We, however, easily deceive ourselves, so when we are tried, when we have to choose not to eat a particular food simply because it doesn't sit right in our spirits, then we learn the reality of our profession. This, in turn, causes us either to rejoice in the work God has already wrought in our hearts through His Holy Spirit, or else to cast ourselves upon His grace more fully. Food (for many believers) is a very practical, easily monitored way of God letting us know the true condition of our hearts! At times we will discover that we fall far short in our consecration; that (like Paul) the good we will to do, we do not, or that the evil we wish not to do, that we do! (see Romans 7:13–23). But this is no reason for us to become condemned. We are learning to walk by faith not by performance. When we fall down, either by what we eat, or how

much, this is a time for us to humble ourselves in repentance and to receive cleansing. Then we resolve to listen all
the more intently and walk on, ever mindful of our perpet-
ual need of God's grace.

4. *Learn about nutrition.* I have already cited a number of
instances from my own life where, through my own personal reading, I have made decisions about what and what
not to eat. We do not have to be so heavenly minded that
we ignore the clear commonsense warnings of health spe-
cialists. As I have sought God to help me become a good
steward of this body He has given me, I have come to realise
that many of the foods we consume have little or no nutritive value, while others contain a wealth of vitamins, minerals and other nutrients which my body needs to function
properly.

While not completely cutting out the former, I have
found as time has gone on that I desire fewer and fewer of
these less nutritive kinds of food; in fact my body sometimes
rejects the very foods that it once embraced! I remember
distinctly the one and only time, since submitting my
appetite to God, that I chose (with complete peace in my
heart) to eat a beefburger at a restaurant. I ordered it complete with white bun and chips! (I reasoned, since I was eating in a restaurant rather than at a fast-food outlet, it may
be more nutritious.) Now it had been more than a year
since I had eaten one and I thought that I would enjoy it as
a treat. But I didn't! It was a real disappointment and I
ended up leaving much of it. I had prayed about choosing
it, so there was no condemnation at all. But as I walked
away from my half-eaten burger, my disappointment

changed to praise, as I realised how much God had changed my tastebuds and desires. I am sure that He will do the same for you, if you will let Him. Several months later I had a similar experience with fast-food fries. Now I know that I am missing very little!

As you learn about nutrition you may find that there comes a point where you start to feel that nothing is really safe, or that our food is so badly depleted of essential minerals that we need to augment our diet with large doses of manufactured supplements. I really do not want to be prescriptive concerning these matters. Some people feel that they should take extra vitamins and minerals and others take no supplements at all. To some degree this issue may be decided by your bank balance, because taking supplements can be very costly. But again I urge you to take the matter to God in prayer and then do what seems right for you, all the time being prepared to alter your stance as time goes on should you receive more light on the matter. Remember that, just as with manufactured diet foods, the bottom line for the manufacturers of supplements is profit, so be prepared for bias if the information is linked to trying to sell you a specific product.

The More Excellent Way

Is it more virtuous to eat carrot sticks than a roast potato? Is it 'better' to eat plain low-fat yoghurt than ice-cream? Well, it all depends on your perspective. If we are looking at this purely from a nutrition point of view, then the carrot sticks and the yoghurt clearly have more going for them. But when we include hunger and satisfaction in the equation, the perspective changes in that it is perhaps more virtuous to eat the roast potato or ice-cream if you are hungry than to eat the carrot sticks and low-fat yoghurt when you are not!

To eat in total freedom is, I believe, God's highest for His children, but if you grasp hold of this particular principle without laying hold of the two principles highlighted in the previous chapter, you could be in trouble! It is vital – if you are to lose weight – that you enjoy this freedom within the bounds of your hunger and satisfaction levels. Initially, however, you could count it a success if you are able to eat in freedom *without* putting weight on! This demonstrates that you are taking some personal responsibility and being freed from a diet mentality even though your understanding of your own body's needs is still minimal. You are learning to juggle three balls in the air, and it will take time for you to manage them all skilfully. This is why I introduced the ideas of eating to your hunger and satisfaction levels first. When you can juggle these two balls skilfully then you are ready to add the third. But do what you feel is best for yourself, and above all be patient, operating within the boundaries of your own faith. Rome wasn't built in a day!

True Enjoyment Leads to True Satisfaction

In an earlier chapter we discussed how the whole of our being is involved in the eating process; that there is an interaction of all our faculties of body, soul and spirit. In this chapter we have concentrated on what foods to choose and have seen that for complete satisfaction it isn't sufficient simply to fill our stomachs. If we do not enjoy the food we eat, we can never be truly satisfied, no matter how much we consume. To experience true satisfaction we need not only physical satisfaction, but mental and emotional satisfaction also. In fact, if we have the added satisfaction of having eaten with a conscious sense of God's leading, even our spirits are refreshed by the experience.

There is perhaps more of a physical reason for this than we at first realise. The hypothalamus in the brain not only controls our appetite and food intake, but is also the control centre for our feelings, emotions and moods. Doesn't it stand to reason, therefore, that we can never be satisfied with food we didn't want?

In our next chapter we shall consider the fourth Fit For Life Forever principle, which has to do with our eating environment, and we will see how important this also is in producing, within us, that feeling of all-round satisfaction.

Home Assignments

1. In what ways have your own negative beliefs concerning food and eating advice given rise to negative emotions?

2. Make a list of your top ten favourite foods. Put a cross besides those which you would normally have considered off-limits to someone wanting to lose weight. (You may have ten crosses!)

3. Pray about these foods and, providing that you (a) have peace and (b) are physiologically hungry, give yourself permission to eat them without guilt. Enjoy!

4. Chose one of your top ten favourite foods and try and classify it according to its flavour, temperature, texture and colour.

5. When you have been practising eating in freedom for a little time answer these questions:

   a. How do you feel, eating with such freedom of choice?

   b. Are you enjoying these foods only within the bounds of your hunger and satisfaction levels?

   c. Have you been able to leave some of your favourite foods once you knew that your hunger was satisfied?

   d. What could you do (in partnership with the Holy Spirit) to improve your measure of control?

   e. Now that you are beginning to eat according to these principles, how does it feel?

14

Creating the Right Environment

The first step to having a Spirit-controlled appetite it is to submit your appetite to God, which we have already talked about in some length. The second step is to invite the Holy Spirit to show us just where our own problems lie in relation to food and eating. He is the Spirit of Truth and desires to lead us into all truth, for it is only by knowing the truth that we can be set free (John 8:32). Once we have the knowledge or understanding, then this same Holy Spirit will grant us the wisdom and power we need to effect whatever changes God requires of us.

In order to learn from the Holy Spirit we need to listen. This is why creating the right environment is so important: it is as we eat that God will make us aware of the thoughts and emotions that govern the way we behave. He will gently prompt us to tell us that we have eaten enough, He will direct us as to how to avoid or resist temptation, and He will show us those unhelpful thought patterns or emotions which make us want to eat inappropriately.

If you look back at the Meal Observation Log which you completed after Chapter 1 you will recall that you were asked to describe the atmosphere and setting you were eating in. Now you are going to learn how to improve your eating environment so that you can listen to your body, and the Holy Spirit, more attentively.

Avoid Distractions

How can God help us to become more conscious of our eating if we are unable to concentrate on our food or His gentle voice? If we eat on the run, grabbing a bite as we rush around doing other things, or if we passively shovel food into our mouths while our attention is focused on some TV programme, then we will not be sensitive to His leading. And yet this is how many of us do eat much of the time.

The Bible says that to everything there is a season, and a time for every purpose under heaven (Ecclesiastes 3:1). Well that includes eating and watching TV! I am not saying that it is absolutely wrong to eat and watch TV at the same time, but what I am saying, following our scriptural principle outlined in 1 Corinthians 6:12–13 and 10:23 is that what is permissible may not always be helpful or sensible when considered against 'other things'. In this case the 'other things' are becoming more self-aware regarding our eating behaviour and hearing the voice of God.

Watching TV is usually a passive form of entertainment. Although our eyes and ears are engaged in watching and listening, no response from us is required, so it is easy to switch our minds onto autopilot and to eat without hardly noticing or tasting what is on our plate. The fork automatically lifts the food to our mouth, the mouth automatically opens and the jaw automatically goes up and down to chew it! Our eyes never really see the food, either to appreciate its taste or to register when we have eaten enough. Only when we mindlessly reach for another mouthful and find it isn't there does it register to our brains that we have finished.

I know that this can be very difficult to put into practice, especially when there are others in the household to consider, but if you can manage to switch the TV off when you are eating it will be a real bonus. Maybe you can tweak your mealtime so that a favourite programme isn't missed, or record the programme to view later. And if it is the news that you generally watch while eating, then these days, with many households having access to cable or satellite TV, it is accessible 24/7, so it isn't any big deal to go without it while you eat.

When you turn the TV off you may well discover something else besides your capacity to hear God – the lost art of conversation! Felicity Lawrence writes: 'In our rush to remove the labour from feeding ourselves, we have lost the cultural significance of meals. It [is] not just about fuel, it [is] the focus of human interaction.'[1] The meal table is a wonderful place for the family to share together, in a light-hearted way, the joys and troubles, the highs and lows, the extraordinary and mundane happenings of our day. This is totally different to passively watching a TV soap, because we listen in order to respond and speak in order to be heard. But we will still be well advised to put our knife and fork down when we are speaking and not to try to do both jobs at once! Having prayed for the Lord to make us aware as we eat, we can still be receptive to His voice speaking to our

---

[1] Lawrence, Felicity, *Not on the Label* (Penguin, 2004)

spirit, even while we are talking and listening to others.

The TV can be a real problem to folk who generally eat alone. Mealtimes can seem especially lonely, and having the TV on seems to provide us with some semblance of having company. But why not try having some music playing instead? Christian songs would be great, but any kind of music with a positive feel would do. A study carried out by Dr Maria Simonson, director of the health, weight and stress programme at the Johns Hopkins University School of Medicine in the US, discovered that people ate less when listening to classical music. In the experiment those who tuned into an upbeat 60s song, for instance, ate about five forkfuls a minute, took 30 minutes to finish their meal and asked for seconds. Those listening to gentle classical music ate three forkfuls a minute and took almost an hour to finish the same meal![2]

Sit at a Table

Apparently, in the UK, sales figures for dining tables and chairs have gone down some 30% over the last 20 years, while the sales of all other kinds of furniture have increased. This would seem to indicate that sitting down at a table to eat is becoming a thing of the past in many households. Sometimes there simply isn't the space in modern houses for a dining suite.

But I would really encourage you to try to make the time to always sit down when you eat. Eating in a rush, while

---

[2] Quoted in Wansink and Chan, 'Exploring Comfort Preferences Across Age and Gender', in *Physiology and Behaviour* (December 2003)

you collect together the things that you need for your next commitment, be it the day's work or some evening activity, isn't only a distraction to hearing the Lord's voice, but is also bad for the digestive process and is more likely to produce tension and negative emotions within you – not what you need when you are trying to regulate your weight.

When we eat consciously at a table, our senses take in the rich variety of aromas, colours and textures and our meal-times become emotionally much more satisfying. Then, as we enjoy God's bounty, and eat the foods we really like in complete freedom, without any guilt or condemnation, and as we hear and respond to the Holy Spirit's inner voice, so our eating involves us on a spiritual level as well. Practise this and you will find more pleasure in eating than you ever thought possible, and you won't want to eat more than your body really needs.

Make your Mealtimes Special

We all know how emotionally satisfying it is when we go out for dinner, either in a restaurant or at a friend's, and see the efforts which have been taken to make it special. . . dinner mats and/or a tablecloth; attractive crockery; flowers or a table ornament; soft music, etc. There is no reason why we can't do this from time to time when we sit down to a main meal in our own home, even if it is only shepherd's pie.

As our family was growing up, my husband, David, and I would sometimes arrange to have our own candlelight dinner. Instead of eating with the children, we would feed them separately and then eat together, just the two of us, once they were in bed. Inevitably there were times when they came downstairs and saw us eating in this way, and accepted it as a part of our life. Then, one day when Tim, our eldest, was about eight years old, David had to go away for a prolonged ministry trip abroad. Tim and I were talking together about missing Daddy, when Tim came up with an idea: 'Let's have a special candlelight supper,' he suggested. 'Okay,' I replied, 'You choose what we shall eat and we'll do it!' He wanted to cook the meal himself so he looked through his *Mr Men Cookbook* and chose something he really liked out of it. Then he took out our best placemats, laid the table just so, and put an artificial flower arrangement in the centre. Finally he got out the perfumed candle, lit it and dimmed the main lights. As we sat down to eat, he remembered the music and put on something he knew I enjoyed in this setting. 'There you are,' he said. 'Just like when Daddy is here.' It wasn't *quite* the same, you understand, but good enough! That goes down as one of the best romantic suppers I've ever had!

It takes time and trouble to organise a meal like this, and if we don't plan it into our schedule then it probably won't happen; but what an enjoyment when we do. Eat the foods you love the most, but keep your portions small enough so that you can enjoy it all without having to forego any of it. If you live alone, invite friends round and make the evening just as special.

Even if you are not pushing the boat out you can still make even the commonest of meals that bit more attractive, so that sitting down to eat is something to look forward to. We always use placemats, even though our regular kitchen table has a wipe-down surface; I always have the cruets and sauces on the table ready at hand, and I often put the food in tureens rather than serving it straight onto our plates. Why? Simply because it looks more attractive. I even make sure that the kitchen door is shut so that it is cosier and we don't have to look out onto the hallway while we eat. If there is clutter on the kitchen counter, I try and make a point of at least straightening it out a little.

Avoid Stressful Conversation

Have you ever noticed that when advertisers on TV want to sell you some food produce they often show a happy family all sitting down together round the table? When the food item is produced (usually by the mother who emerges triumphantly from the kitchen), everybody notices, their eyes light up and they grin from ear to ear in rapturous anticipation! On the other hand, TV soaps will often depict the meal table as a place where dissensions arise, tempers flare and somebody storms out! The first scenario may seem ideal and fairly unrealistic; the second, sad to say, may be closer to the truth.

If you are upset or anxious and have been brooding on it all day, it is very tempting, once you are sitting down at the meal table and have a captive audience, to just pour it all out. This produces tension and may end up as an all-out row – hardly the best eating experience! Or maybe you are the quiet type who prefers to punish others by your silence. You say nothing, but your face and non-communicative attitude leave others in no doubt that you are miffed over something. 'What's up?' someone proffers, but you just shrug your shoulders and refuse to reply.

When negative emotions are stirred up or when we are fearful about where a conversation might be heading, this

often produces a physical sensation within us. Our stomachs knot up and we may actually find it harder to eat.
Imagine what this is doing to our digestive system! We push
the food away, refusing or feeling unable to eat any more and
leave the table. Later on, as we bring to memory the unhappy
experience we have had over the meal table, the pain of
things that were said comes back to us and we take solace
by bingeing on some comfort food. Does this ring any bells?

There is a time and place for everything, and the meal
table should be a time for positive conversation and
affirmations. In fact, if you do have some things to iron out,
far better to do this before the meal, so that forgiveness can
flow and you can enjoy the food in a relaxed way. This isn't
only applicable between adults; it applies to your children
as well. If you wish them to grow up wanting to continue
sitting together with you as a family, then they need to
know that you are not going to use this time to deliver a sermon on keeping their room tidy, being more thoughtful or
such like. You will be surprised at how much more satisfying the meal can be when you discipline yourself to being
positive in your speech.

Our Victorian forebears often displayed a religious plaque
above their dining table which read: 'Christ is the Head of
this house, the unseen guest at every meal, the silent listener to every conversation.' The plaque itself may be out
of vogue, but the truth remains. The Gospels record some
wonderful times of Jesus sharing a meal with His disciples
and others. Remembering that He abides with us today,
even as we share our food, is itself a great blessing.

Home Assignments

1. Turn to the log entitled, My Eating Environment, which is found in Appendix 5. This exercise will help you to become more aware of the dynamics which surround your mealtimes, and together with the teaching of this chapter will help you to re-order your life to gain the maximum benefit from your eating and further the fulfilment of your weight goals.

2. What changes could you make to your eating environment which might make you more aware of how you eat?

3. What are the difficulties that you might encounter as you seek to bring about some changes? Pray about these things.

15

A Spirit-controlled Appetite

What we have been aiming for throughout this book is a Spirit-controlled appetite. This is just another facet to the Spirit-controlled life which should be the lifestyle of every Christian believer. As with everything else in our spiritual walk, we find this to be a process in which the Holy Spirit first reveals to us what is 'of the flesh' in our lives, brings it to an end through the cross and then imparts His own strength and ability so that it is 'no longer I who live, but Christ who lives in me' (Galatians 2:20). What a freedom and joy it brings when our appetites, so basic to our everyday lives and existence, are brought under the Spirit's control and we no longer need to strive in our own strength to bring order and control into our eating.

For any change of behaviour to become a permanent part of your life it has to become a habit. To a great extent your patterns of overeating or eating for inappropriate reasons have been the result of various acquired habits which began in your mind and emotions and then became conditioned responses to various stimuli. Now this has all got to change, and hopefully – if you have not only been reading but also seeking to apply the teaching of this book – there are already some positive outcomes in your life. For ease of understanding and application I have focused separately on the various aspects of eating as they relate to our physical bodies, mind, will, emotions and inner spirit, but when we eat every part of our being comes into play simultaneously. Now is the time to bring it all together so that you can develop positive habits which will stay with you forever.

What is a Habit?

A habit is an acquired behaviour pattern regularly followed until it has become almost involuntary. The word itself is derived from the Latin and means literally 'clothing which is usually worn' – hence its application to the garment worn by members of a religious order. Habits are, in fact, practices which we wrap around our life.

We generally talk about 'good habits' and 'bad habits', but what constitutes this distinction? I would maintain that good habits are those which give us peace and a sense of wellbeing and help us to develop and realise our dreams and goals. Bad habits, on the other hand, take away our peace of mind, they block our progress and impair our efforts to reach our goals. Developing a good habit involves doing the right thing for the right reason on a continuous basis and will, eventually, produce attitudes and behaviours which become part and parcel of our lives.

Not everyone who reads this book will lose weight! Just as hidden treasure may not be found by the casual seeker, so neither can weight regulation be achieved by any half-hearted approach. Spiritual progress is only achieved by seeking God with all of our heart and, since this is a book about having a Spirit-controlled appetite, the same principle needs to be applied. If you are to become an intuitive eater, using food only to satisfy your physiological needs, then the changes put forward in this book need to become positive habits. This will require 100% commitment.

This will be evidenced firstly by a deep desire to change, which may come out of desperation regarding your own shape and size or your health, or it may be born out of a conviction of the Holy Spirit that you are not glorifying God in your body the way He requires. Then you will need a realistic goal, both for your weight and, more importantly, your health. If you haven't done so already, you should be praying about the weight that God wants you to be, which will generally be within the 'normal' bracket of the BMI scale. You will also need personal action plans for applying the principles in this book, which involves praying over all the issues as they apply to you and asking God to show you what He requires *personally* from you by way of response.

Elimination and Reinforcement

To achieve all of the above you will need to develop strategies which will help you overcome all obstacles to your progress and this, realistically, includes failure. There are broadly two types of strategy: those which will help you to *eliminate* inappropriate behaviour with negative outcomes and those which will *reinforce* appropriate behaviour which has positive outcomes. Let us address these separately.

It is essential that you observe closely your own eating behaviour, which is why completing the various charts in this book are so important. Then you need to evaluate your own eating behaviour in terms of your own goals – is it helping or hindering your progress? If you observe that certain behaviour is unhelpful, then you need to reflect on which factors may have triggered it – this means asking the question 'Why am I eating this?' You may conclude that you are eating simply because food is available or because of your false or unhelpful thoughts and emotions. It may be connected to the time of day, the environment or company you are keeping or the activities you are (or are not) engaged in, or it may due to physical factors such as a prevailing illness, fatigue or the medication you are on.

Once you have analysed your behaviour in this way you need to decide what factors can be controlled and which cannot. For instance, you may have to take your lunch hour at a specific time, or you may have to spend time alone, which leaves you vulnerable. Don't blame yourself for those things which you can't control, but determine to be proactive about the things which you can.

Now, having observed your unhelpful responses, you need to replace them with something more helpful, but it is no good thinking about this when the temptation has arisen – it is then too late! Rather, you need to think ahead and have a strategy prepared in advance. So, I want you to anticipate a similar set of circumstances to those you have been considering. Ask yourself what things you might be able to change and how. Then, the next time that the same situation arises you are forearmed with a new response. Try it out and see if it works. If it still doesn't work, don't be discouraged; just go back to the drawing board. Reflect again on the various factors involved, thus seeking to bring about further modifications to the way you behave. Keep doing this in a conscious way and eventually you will succeed.

When you try out a new strategy and see that it works, reflect on what it was that enabled you to succeed. Was it that you were thinking differently, or was your speech more positive? Did you perhaps change your environment (like avoiding going past the snack machine) or find something different to do which took your mind off food? Did you pray? Whatever it was that worked for you, just keep on doing it. In this way you are reinforcing what works and helping it to become a new habit in your life.

A Case Scenario

To help you understand these techniques of elimination and reinforcement, here is a case scenario you may be able to identify with, at least in part. It involves a typical family evening meal. . .

It's a weekday evening. You have come in from work around 4pm, starving because you weren't able to eat properly at lunchtime. You grab the nearest thing at hand which is a packet of crisps, followed by a snack bar, bought especially for your children's packed lunch.

Your partner / husband / wife comes in from work around 6pm and likes to have the meal ready and waiting. You have to get out to a meeting yourself for 7pm so you prepare something simple and easy – chicken kiev, peas and chips – acceptable to all the family. You dish out the food, giving yourself the usual sized portion.

You all sit down to the evening meal, watching the news on TV at the same time, and trying to catch up with any family news. You have one eye on the clock because you have to be out in 20 minutes and have yet to get ready.

You eat quickly, hardly being conscious of the meal except that you are feeling somewhat overfull towards the end of it. You could leave what you don't need, but it seems a shame to throw it away and none of it would keep well for another day, so you finish the lot.

You wouldn't have thought about dessert except that the children want ice-cream and so, too, does your partner. You dish it out for them and it looks good, so you decide that you don't want to be left out and give yourself a helping as well, plus the caramel topping and ready-whipped cream.

You rush it down, because now you only have five minutes to get ready, so the moment you've finished the dish you're on your feet, up and out. You arrive at the meeting feeling stuffed, lethargic and mad at yourself for having eaten so much.

What Factors Triggered the Overeating?	*Could These be Changed? Yes or No?*
■ General rushing around – at lunch and again in the evening.	*Yes and No!*
■ Feeling 'starving' when you came in from work.	*No*
■ The family's needs to be fed at a specific time.	*No*
■ The need to prepare something 'quick and easy' that is processed, high in fat and carbohydrates.	*Yes*
■ Eating with distractions – TV.	*Yes*

- Habitual serving size regardless   *Yes*
  of appetite.
- Thought of leaving good food   *Yes*
  seemed unacceptable.
- Wanting dessert with all the   *Yes*
  trimmings.

What Might You Have Changed?

- Anticipate the rush. Prepare something like a casserole ahead of time.
- Set yourself rules regarding the children's snacks or don't have them in the house.
- Have something healthy at hand for such emergencies when you feel hungry but can't have your meal, like fruit or a small piece of cheese.
- Give yourself a smaller portion, especially the chips! Promise yourself the dessert later *if* you are hungry.
- Turn off the TV.
- Leave the dessert and let others serve it out. You go and get ready.

This approach of elimination and reinforcement can be approached on a purely natural level, but when you involve God in this whole exercise it will greatly enhance your ability to succeed. Here are some ways in which a spiritual dimension can be added:

- Ask the Holy Spirit to show you the truth about your behaviour and the factors affecting it.
- Repent of any wrong attitudes and behaviour.

- Renew your thoughts in accordance with the truth of God's word.
- Know and accept your own inability to achieve good results in your own strength and receive the empowerment of the Holy Spirit so that you will, by grace, be able to obey whatever He shows you to do.
- Yield yourself completely to God so that He can continually heal your emotions and meet your inner hunger.
- Have faith! Learn to doubt your doubts and hold fast to the truth of God's word.

Home Assignments

1. Seek to enforce all the strategies shown to you in this chapter in relation to your own daily life. You might like to write out a day's diary similar to the one above and then analyse it to see what you could change and what you could not. Be thorough!
2. Reflect on what new habits are already being woven into your eating behaviour. Write these down and turn it into praise and thanksgiving to God.

16

Fit For Life – FOREVER

The whole aim of this book has been to replace your previous diet mentality, with all of its accompanying agony, hang-ups and impossible performance goals, with that of an intuitive eater who uses food appropriately and thus becomes the shape and size which God fore-ordained. Of course, I hope that it will have achieved far more, and this has been the testimony of so many who have followed these principles. Commonly, people who have completed this course have found an inner freedom which goes far deeper than issues surrounding food. Freed from their preoccupation with food they have discovered new ways of directing their mental and physical energies; as their self-esteem has been raised and emotional hurts from the past have been healed, so their confidence has grown and they have been able to reach out more effectively to others. For many, the way in which they have related to food has served as a spiritual barometer, highlighting areas of their life where they still needed to submit to the Holy Spirit. Not only have their eating habits changed, but their whole spiritual life has progressed as inner hungers have been satisfied through a deeper walk with the Lord.

Whatever our particular need or circumstance, learning to live as an intuitive eater involves five distinct things. These are: a process, struggles, a paradigm shift, a new relationship with food and internalised control. Let us look briefly at each of these.

A Process

There is an old Chinese proverb which says, 'The journey of a thousand miles begins with the first step.' One verse of Scripture which complements this is that of Paul in Philippians 3:13–14, where he writes, 'Forgetting what lies behind . . . I press on toward the goal. . . ' Fit For Life Forever involves a steady process; it is not a quick fix. For many following the course, weight loss has become secondary. Since the change is from the inside out, weight loss may not happen immediately. Even with total commitment, the time it takes will depend largely upon the type of root cause which has needed the greatest attention. Emotional hurts from the past often take longer to surface and be healed than, for instance, eating due to boredom. Excessive eating due to faulty, unhelpful thinking, is perhaps easier to address than a stronghold of lust, but each one of us is different. What you *can* expect (except perhaps in the case of medical anomalies) is that, in time, your weight will be released until your BMI is within the normal range and your waist circumference is no more than 37 inches (men), or 31.5 inches (women). But you may need a year, at least – it will depend on how much you need to lose. You will find that you are increasingly in control of your food management and this will further enhance your sense of freedom and self-esteem. You will be wonderfully free from your preoccupation with food.

Struggles

By struggles, I mean that it isn't all going to be plain sailing and that you will undoubtedly experience setbacks of one form or another. 'Always remember that striving and struggle precede success, even in the dictionary!'[1] Thank God that we do not need to struggle and strive in our own strength, but that God empowers us as we continually look to Him in our weakness. We find, like the apostle Paul, that when we are weak, then we are strong (2 Corinthians 12:10). The greatest obstacle you will need to overcome is probably that of failure, not so much because of the failure itself but because it is so often used by the devil to discourage us to the point of giving up. Failure, however, can be transformed into success if we will learn from it – this was the focus of our last chapter.

Also, remember that failure is an event; it is not a person. You may fail, but that does not make *you* a failure. Refuse to accept this lie. Winston Churchill once said: 'Success is the ability to go from failure to failure without losing your enthusiasm.'[2] Scripturally this is embodied in the injunction not to lose heart. Why can we maintain hope in the

---

[1] Ban Breathnach, Sarah, on the Success Methods website: www.successmethods.org/success-quotes.html (accessed 28/11/06)

[2] Churchill, Winston, on the Said What? website: www.said-what.co.uk/quotes/political/success (accessed 10/12/06)

face of setbacks? Because He who has begun a good work in us is faithful to perform it (Philippians 1:6). Hang on to this verse. You may not yet be where you want to be, but you are also not where you started. Rejoice in this and remain patient.

A Paradigm Shift

The word 'paradigm' may be defined as a model or frame of reference by which we perceive and understand the world. When we speak of a 'paradigm shift', what this implies is that there is a change in one's way of thinking so that it produces a profound and irreversible change of behaviour or perception. Through the teaching of this book you may, depending upon your starting point, have been faced with new paradigms in three areas: food and diets, God and your self-image.

Food and Diets

The old paradigm told you that the only way to lose weight was to go on a diet. You also believed, maybe only subconsciously, that food was meant to be the answer to multiple needs in your life, not just physiological hunger. Now you know that, for most of us, diets do not work and that food is meant primarily to meet physical hunger and can never meet other needs for which it was never intended.

God

You may have come to this book believing either that God does not exist or, if He does, He is irrelevant to your life with respect to what and how much you eat. You may also have believed that there is no power outside of yourself to help you achieve your weight goals. Now, I hope, you not only believe in the reality of God, but are coming to appreciate how profoundly interested He is in all aspects of your life, including the way in which you relate to food and eating. Also, I trust that you are beginning to experience for yourself His grace and power being released into your life to help you to live according to His word. 'I can do all things through Him who strengthens me' (Philippians 4:13).

Self-image

So many of our problems concerning food are an expression of a faulty self-image. Maybe you used to define your identity as 'fat' and ate accordingly. Now, because your mental attitudes have changed, you already see yourself as a thin person and are beginning to eat according to your new, biblical self-image, even if your outer person portrays one who is still obese. Once your eating was controlled by external circumstances, but now you are learning to take control of your body and your eating habits. Once your self-esteem and self-worth were based on how well you performed and were measured against the expectations of others; now you know that these things are based on who you are by creation and how you look in God's eyes – which is beautiful.

A New Relationship With Food

Your new relationship with food can be summed up in just three words: *Freedom from bondage!* As you have allowed God to shine His truth into your life, so it is that knowing that truth has set you free. It has been painful at times to remove the mask and to face your problems head on, but it has been worth it. Now, with your whole life, including your appetite, fully yielded to God, you can eat anything you like without needing to count calories or fear gaining weight. This is glorious!

Once you were under the control of gluttony, greed and strong cravings which you could not control, but now, through the merits of what Jesus did on the cross, you are not only forgiven and thus freed from the guilt of such behaviour, you are empowered to live under the control of the Holy Spirit, no longer to fulfil the lusts of the flesh.

Your beliefs concerning food and eating used to be derived from your own culture and traditions or from the wisdom of men; now you have been given the keys to free you from these old, unworkable beliefs so that you can apply the wisdom of God's word to these fundamental areas of your life.

Because of the emotional baggage you were carrying with you from your past, you used to rely on food to help you to cope and make you feel better. Now that you have been freed from the guilt and pain associated with painful past experiences, and your emotions have been healed by the power of God, you no longer need this prop. Food has found its rightful place.

Internalised Control

Think about it – diets, rules, calorie counting, food restrictions, weighing scales – all these are a thing of the past. It isn't that you have cast all restraint to the wind and blow the consequences. No, you are learning to listen to the Holy

Spirit and to trust the messages given by your own body to let you know when and what to eat. You have accepted your own personal responsibility to bring your weight under control and are submitted to the will of God, so as to make wise choices. No longer will you need to slavishly follow anyone's prescribed diet, eating bland food that does not satisfy, or going to unrealistic lengths to try and limit your intake of calories.

Nor are you seeking to regulate your weight because someone else has said that you must. You have decided for yourself that this is what *you* wanted to do. Your weight goal is what *you* decided, in consultation with the Holy Spirit. What, when and how much you eat is governed, not by the clock, not by traditions, not by economics, not by guilt; nor is it governed by your husband / wife, parents, children or even your doctor – it is governed by *you*, in partnership with the Living God. All of this comes from within, in a spirit of peace, joy, faith and self-control. It is, in fact, the fruit of the Spirit spoken of in Galatians 5:22–23.

A Journey of Discovery

As you have read (perhaps over a period of several weeks if you have been following the Fit For Life Forever study plan) you have been on an exciting journey of discovery. You have learnt not only how your body works and relates to food but also how eating is a holistic experience, involving body, mind, emotions and your inner spirit. You may have been taken by surprise as you have become increasingly self-aware regarding your own previous self-destructive relationship with food, but this has been tempered by an increasing knowledge of how much God is both willing and able to help put things right.

So far we have come, but your journey is far from over. Even if you have reached your weight goal, it is my prayer that this book will have served to open up many other areas of your life for your personal and spiritual development. Eternal life is the gift of God to all who will believe, not only for beyond the grave, but beginning here and now. To enjoy this life in all its fullness we need to be fit and this involves the committed stewardship of our physical bodies so that we remain healthy and strong. Then we truly will be 'fit for life forever'.

Home Assignments

1. Now is a good time to check your progress. If it doesn't scare you too much, you may want to weigh yourself and reassess your new BMI, waist measurement and associated health risks. How are your clothes feeling?

2. Would you say that you are becoming increasingly in control of your eating? In what ways?

3. Are you less preoccupied with food than you were at the start?

4. Have you experienced any of the paradigm shifts spoken of in this chapter? In what ways have your beliefs about food, yourself and God changed throughout this course?

5. Share all that you have been learning with a friend and introduce them to Fit For Life Forever.

6. Consult the website: www.f4lf.org for support materials to help you continue to develop a Spirit-controlled appetite.

Appendix 1 – Meal Observation Log

Time of meal: ....

Category: *breakfast / lunch / tea / dinner / supper*

How long since your last meal? ....

What snacks or drinks have you taken in between? ......
....

Describe the atmosphere / setting you ate in: ....

Where were you? ....

Did you sit at a table to eat? *Yes / No* ....

Were you: a*lone / with others: family / friends / work associates?*

Did you put your fork down at all while you ate? *Yes / No*

Did you eat: *fast / moderately / slowly?*

Were there distractions? eg *TV, phone calls, visitors, much noise*. ....

Was the atmosphere: *cordial / neutral / tense / hostile / other:* .
....

How hungry were you when you sat down to eat? *very / quite / a little / not really / not at all*

If you were not hungry, what was your reason for eating? *regular mealtime / fitting in with others' schedules / invited out / may not have time later / convenience / other reasons* ....

What did you eat? (please list all food / drink) ....
....

Did you a) *really* taste each mouthful of food or b) eat automatically with your mind on other things?

Underline those foods on your list that you *really* enjoyed.

Was there any food that you didn't enjoy but ate anyway? *Yes / No*

If yes – why did you eat it? . . . .

. . . .

Did you have seconds or eat off other people's plates? *Yes / No*

If yes, why? . . . .

Did you overeat? *Yes / No*

Did you leave anything on your plate? *Yes / No*

If yes, why? . . . .

Was there any food left over from the meal? *Yes / No*

If so, what happened to it? . . . .

How long did the meal last? . . . .

Was your hunger satisfied when you had finished the meal? *Yes / No*

Did you feel any guilt associated with eating? *Yes / No*

If yes, can you say why? . . . .

How would you rate your overall meal experience? *enjoyable / satisfactory / not enjoyable*

If you could have changed anything about the meal experience, what would it have been . . . .

Appendix 2 – Emotional Eating Log

What you ate	How you felt	What you were doing	Time of day

Appendix 3 – Reasons for Eating Log

Follow the example given below and for several days keep a record of those times when you eat outside your main mealtimes. Try to discover your reason for eating and the possible root. Use the examples given below as a guide.

Time of day	Reason for eating	Root cause of behaviour
Mid-morning	Staff birthday – doughnuts all round – don't want to miss out	Sensory: couldn't resist. Mental: it's free – take it!
Home from work	It was a hard day – I felt stressed out	Emotional: comfort / reward
Evening meal	Ate leftovers rather than throw them away	Mental: 'wrong' to waste it
Evening out to cinema	Popcorn – I always eat this at the cinema	Habitual response

Appendix 4 – Hunger and Satisfaction Log

This week you are asked to keep a log of your hunger and satisfaction levels at mealtimes for at least three days. I am assuming that you would eat three times a day, but if you omit a meal (which is okay if you are not hungry), leave that row blank.

Take meal 1. Assess how hungry you are when you start to eat and tick that column. At the end of the meal enter a second tick to show how full you felt.

	-1	Empty	¼	½	¾	Satis-fied	=1	+2	+3 stuffed
Meal 1									
Meal 2									
Meal 3									
Meal 4									
Meal 5									
Meal 6									
Meal 7									
Meal 8									
Meal 9									

Appendix 5 – My Eating Environment

Using a tally system (ticking according to frequency) complete this chart over a period of a few consecutive days. It will help you to recognise negative aspects of your eating atmosphere and to create ones which will help you to succeed in your weight management goals.

a) Where you ate

	Breakfast	Lunch	Evening
At a table			
On a sofa			
Standing up			
On the run			
In the office			
Didn't eat			

b) Setting

	Breakfast	Lunch	Evening
Attractive			
Tidy / not attractive			
Untidy			

c) Distractions

	Breakfast	Lunch	Evening
No distraction			
Telephone			
TV			
Radio			

d) Conversations

	Breakfast	Lunch	Evening
None			
Amicable / positive			
Stressful / negative			